student WORKBOOK

A2 Chemistry Multiple Choice

Introduction

This book of multiple-choice and short-answer questions is intended as a revision aid. Having covered a topic area, you can quickly check your understanding by completing the relevant test.

The key areas of A2 chemistry are:
■ Organic chemistry
■ Transition metal chemistry
■ Physical chemistry

For each area there are tests on the key topics, followed by a general test, which covers the whole area. Each multiple-choice question is followed by a short-answer question, resulting in 18 multiple-choice questions and short-answer questions in each test.

It should take you 50 minutes to complete a test. The multiple-choice questions are worth 1 mark each, while the short-answer questions are worth 2 marks. On the next page is a grid on which you can chart your progress.

Progress check

Topic area	Multiple choice		Short answers	
	Possible score	Your score	Possible score	Your score
Organic chemistry				
Aromatic chemistry	18		36	
Carbonyl chemistry	18		36	
Carboxylic acids and amines	18		36	
Spectroscopy	18		36	
General questions	18		36	
Total	**90**		**180**	
Transition metal chemistry				
Transition metals and complexes	18		36	
Redox chemistry and catalysis	18		36	
The chemistry of selected transition metals	18		36	
General questions	18		36	
Total	**72**		**144**	
Physical chemistry				
Enthalpy changes and periodicity	18		36	
Rates of reaction	18		36	
The equilibrium law	18		36	
Acid–base equilibria	18		36	
General questions	18		36	
Total	**90**		**180**	
OVERALL TOTAL	**252**		**504**	

Organic chemistry

Aromatic chemistry

1 Which of A–E would be appropriate conditions for this chemical transformation?

    ☐ A   ☐ B   ☐ C   ☐ D   ☐ E

What is the molecular formula of benzene?

....

....

2 Which of A–E would be appropriate conditions for this chemical transformation?

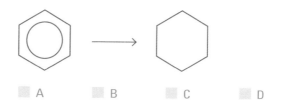

    ☐ A   ☐ B   ☐ C   ☐ D   ☐ E

Name the mechanism for this reaction.

....

....

3 Which of A–E would be appropriate conditions for this chemical transformation?

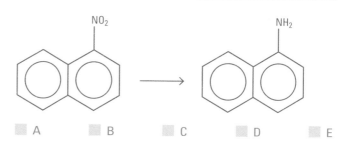

    ☐ A   ☐ B   ☐ C   ☐ D   ☐ E

What is the molecular formula of the product in this reaction?

....

....

4 Which of A–E would be appropriate conditions for this chemical transformation?

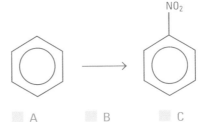

☐ A ☐ B ☐ C ☐ D ☐ E

Give the name and formula of the electrophile in this reaction.

....

....

5 Which of A–E would be appropriate conditions for this chemical transformation?

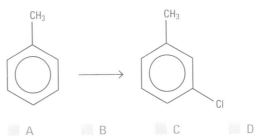

☐ A ☐ B ☐ C ☐ D ☐ E

Name the starting compound in this reaction.

....

....

6

Bond	Bond length/nm	Mean bond energy/kJ mol^{-1}	Choice	Bond length/nm	Mean bond energy/kJ mol^{-1}
C–C	0.154	348	A	Greater than 0.154	Greater than 348
C=C	0.134	612	B	Greater than 0.134	Less than 348
C≡C	0.120	837	C	Greater than 0.120	Greater than 837
			D	Less than 0.120	Less than 837
			E	Less than 0.154	Greater than 348

With reference to the tables, the correct bond length and mean bond energy for the carbon–carbon bond in benzene is:

☐ A ☐ B ☐ C ☐ D ☐ E

What is the value of the internal angle in a benzene ring?

....

....

7

Possible structures of molecules X and Y are:

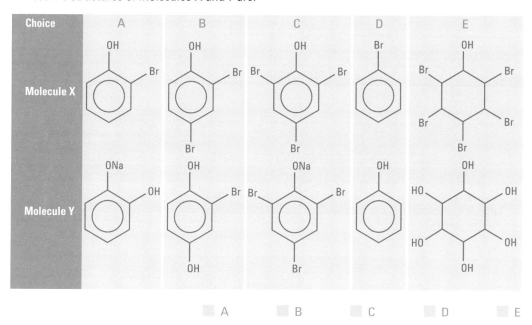

	A	B	C	D	E
	A	B	C	D	E

Name the reaction by which compound X is converted to compound Y.

....

....

8 The empirical formula of the molecule below is:

    A $C_{12}H_{10}O_2$
    B $C_{10}H_8O_2$
    C $C_{10}H_{10}O_2$
    D C_5H_4O
    E C_6H_5O

Will this molecule react with aqueous sodium hydroxide?

....

....

9 The approximate values for the bond angles labelled x and y in a molecule of phenol are:

Choice	Angle x	Angle y
A	90°	90°
B	109.5°	109.5°
C	107°	109.5°
D	104.5°	120°
E	120°	120°

    A   B   C   D   E

Explain why the C–O bond in phenol is shorter than in an aliphatic alcohol.

....

....

10 The mechanism involved in the process below is called:

Cl

$Cl_2/AlCl_3$ →

- A nucleophilic substitution
- B electrophilic substitution
- C nucleophilic addition
- D radical substitution
- E electrophilic addition

What is the formula of the species that attacks the benzene ring in this reaction?

....

....

Instructions for answering
questions 11–16:

A 1, 2 and 3 only are correct
B 1 and 3 only are correct
C 2 and 4 only are correct
D 4 only is correct
E some other response

11 Phenol reacts with bromine faster than benzene does because:
(1) the electron density on the ring in phenol is greater than in benzene
(2) the OH group in phenol has a lone pair of electrons
(3) the lone pair of electrons on the oxygen atom in phenol is delocalised into the ring
(4) phenol behaves as a nucleophile

　　　　　A　　　　　B　　　　　C　　　　　D　　　　　E

What has to be added to benzene in order for it to react with bromine?

....

....

12 True statements about this molecule include:
(1) it is called 5-chloromethylbenzene
(2) the C–Cl bond will not be broken when the molecule is
treated with sodium hydroxide solution and refluxed
(3) nucleophiles will readily attack the ring
(4) the molecular formula of the compound is C_7H_7Cl

CH_3

Cl

　　　　　A　　　　　B　　　　　C　　　　　D　　　　　E

How many positional isomers exist for this compound?

13 Which of the following are electrophiles?
(1) NO_2^+
(2) CH_4
(3) Cl^+
(4) NH_3

        A   B   C   D   E

What is an electrophile?

14

$OH \longrightarrow + H_2O \rightleftharpoons O^- + H_3O^+$

True statements about the dissociation of phenol in water include:
(1) phenol behaves as a base in the reaction
(2) the dissolving process forms an acidic solution
(3) phenol is a strong acid
(4) $C_6H_5O^-$ is the conjugate base of phenol

        A   B   C   D   E

Write an equation that shows the ability of the $C_6H_5O^-$ ion to accept a proton from a water molecule.

15 Which of these chemical tests could be used to distinguish between molecules X and Y?
(1) warming with acidified potassium chromate(VI) solution
(2) adding silver(I) nitrate solution
(3) warming with sodium hydroxide solution
(4) adding bromine water

        A   B   C   D   E

What is the molecular formula for molecule Y?

16 How many structural isomers are there for dichlorobenzene, in which two chlorine atoms are attached to the benzene ring?

(1) 0

(2) 1

(3) 2

(4) 3

     A   B   C   D   E

How can the structural isomers in this question be distinguished?

....

....

Questions 17 and 18 relate to the following mechanism:

17 In the first step of the mechanism, benzene is acting as:

    A a catalyst

    B an acid

    C a nucleophile

    D an oxidising agent

    E an electrophile

Write equations to show how the species NO_2^+ is generated in this mechanism.

....

....

18 The rate equation consistent with the mechanism is:

    A rate $= k[C_6H_6]$

    B rate $= k[C_6H_6][NO_2^+]$

    C rate $= k[C_6H_6]^2$

    D rate $= k[C_6H_6][NO_2^+]^0$

    E rate $= k([C_6H_6] + [NO_2^+])$

What is the link between a simple mechanism and the rate equation for this reaction?

....

....

Carbonyl chemistry

1

Choice	Molecule X	Molecule Y
A	Propan-2-ol	Butanoic acid
B	Propanone	Butanoic acid
C	Propanal	Butanal
D	Propanone	Butanal
E	Pentanone	Butanone

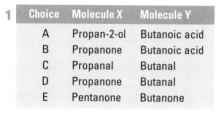

The names of molecules X and Y are:

                     A   B   C   D   E

How can these two compounds be distinguished chemically?

2 The colour change when ethanal is warmed with a few drops of acidified potassium dichromate(VI) solution is:

- A green to yellow
- B yellow to orange
- C green to blue
- D orange to green
- E blue to red

Name this type of reaction.

3

CHO

The organic product when this molecule is treated with ammoniacal silver(I) nitrate solution (Tollens' reagent) is:

- A C_7H_6O
- B $C_7H_6O_2$
- C C_7H_8O
- D C_6H_6O
- E $C_7H_{12}O_2$

Write an equation to show what happens to the silver(I) ion in this reaction.

Questions 4–7 are concerned with the following reaction scheme:

X

$$H-\underset{\underset{H}{|}}{\overset{\overset{H}{|}}{C}}-OH \longrightarrow$$

Y

$$\underset{H}{\overset{H}{>}}C=O \longrightarrow$$

Z

$$\underset{H}{\overset{H}{>}}\underset{CN}{\overset{OH}{C}}$$

4 Which of A–E could transform compound X into compound Y?

  A heating with dilute sodium hydroxide solution

  B adding methanoic acid in the presence of concentrated sulphuric acid

  C adding hydrogen gas and passing the mixture over nickel at 150°C

  D heating with acidified sodium dichromate(VI) solution

  E passing over an aluminium oxide catalyst at 300°C

Name the chemical change undergone by compound X.

....

....

5 The name of the mechanism for the conversion of compound Y into compound Z is:

  A radical substitution

  B nucleophilic addition

  C electrophilic addition

  D oxidation

  E nucleophilic substitution

Is compound Y polar? Explain your answer.

....

....

....

6 Compound Y could be converted into compound Z by:

  A HCN with a trace of KCN

  B NH_3 in ethanol

  C N_2 gas and an iron catalyst at 450°C

  D concentrated sulphuric acid and concentrated nitric acid at 50°C

  E ammoniacal silver(I) nitrate solution

Name compound Y.

....

....

7 When molecule Z is heated with dilute hydrochloric acid, a new compound is formed which has the structure:

  A H, OH, C, H, NH_2

  B H, OH, C, H, CHC

  C O, C, H, CN

  D H, OH, C, H, COOH

  E H, OH, C, H, CH_2OH

Name this type of reaction.

....

....

8 Which of A–E is chiral?

    A $CH_3CH_2CHClCH_2CH_3$
    B $CH_3CH_2OCH_2CHO$
    C $CH_3CH=CHCH_3$
    D $C_6H_5CH(OH)CN$
    E $CH_3CH=CH-CH_2CH_3$

Name the alkane of lowest molecular mass that is chiral.

....

....

Instructions for answering questions 9–13:	A 1, 2 and 3 only are correct
	B 1 and 3 only are correct
	C 2 and 4 only are correct
	D 4 only is correct
	E some other response

9 Samples of butanone and pentanone can be distinguished by:
(1) measuring their boiling points
(2) warming with Tollens' reagent
(3) adding 2,4-dinitrophenylhydrazine and measuring the melting points of the derivatives
(4) warming with acidified sodium dichromate(VI) solution

    A   B   C   D   E

To which class of organic compounds do butanone and pentanone belong?

....

....

10 Which of the following transformations can be achieved using sodium borohydride?

(1) $CH_3CHO \longrightarrow CH_3CH_2OH$ (3)

(2) $CH_3CHO \longrightarrow CH_3COOH$ (4)

    A   B   C   D   E

Explain, in terms of electron transfer, how sodium borohydride reacts.

....

....

11 Butanone and butanal can be distinguished by:

(1) adding 2,4-dinitrophenylhydrazine

(2) warming with ammoniacal silver(I) nitrate

(3) adding sodium metal

(4) warming with acidified potassium dichromate(VI)

    A   B   C   D   E

Using [H] convention, write a half-equation that describes what happens to butanal when it is reduced.

....

....

12 Which of the following equations are relevant when ethanal is warmed with ammoniacal silver(I) nitrate solution?

(1) $Ag^+(aq) + e^- \longrightarrow Ag(s)$

(2) $CH_3CHO + H_2O \longrightarrow CH_3COOH + 2H^+ + 2e^-$

(3) $CH_3CHO + [O] \longrightarrow CH_3COOH$

(4) $CH_3CHO + 2[H] \longrightarrow CH_3CH_2OH$

    A   B   C   D   E

Is ethanal chiral? Explain your answer.

....

....

13 Which of the following will yield chiral products when treated with hydrogen cyanide in the presence of potassium cyanide?

(1) CH_3CHO

(2) CH_3COCH_3

(3) $CH_3COCH_2CH_3$

(4) $CH_3COCH_2COCH_3$ A   B   C   D   E

How can chiral molecules be distinguished from each other?

....

....

Questions 14–16 are concerned with the following mechanism:

14 In the first stage of the mechanism, the cyanide ion is acting as:

    A a base
    B an electrophile
    C a catalyst
    D a proton acceptor
    E a nucleophile

Write an equation to show how hydrogen cyanide reacts with sodium hydroxide solution.

....

....

15 When propanal is used in the reaction, the optical properties of the product are best described by:

    A (+) $CH_3CH_2CH(OH)CN$ only
    B (+) and (−) $CH_3CH_2CH(OH)NH_2$ in equal proportions
    C (+) and (−) $CH_3CH_2CH(OH)CN$ in equal proportions
    D CH_3CH_2COOH only
    E (−) $CH_3CH_2CH(OH)CN$ only

What is meant by the term 'racemic mixture'?

....

....

16 In the second stage, the water molecule is acting as:

    A an acid
    B a hydrating agent
    C a nucleophile
    D a catalyst
    E a base

Write an equation to show the reaction between the methoxide anion, CH_3O^-, and water.

....

....

17

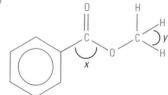

The approximate values for the angles marked x and y in this molecule are:

Choice	Angle x	Angle y
A	109.5°	120°
B	120°	109.5°
C	104.5°	109.5°
D	104.5°	107°
E	120°	90°

    A   B   C   D   E

To which class of organic compounds does the compound in this question belong?

....

....

18 In a typical synthetic route, sodium borohydride acts as:

    A a catalyst
    B a reducing agent
    C a dehydrating agent
    D an oxidising agent
    E an acid

What is the chemical formula for sodium borohydride? Use the formula to deduce the oxidation number of hydrogen in the compound.

Carboxylic acids and amines

1 Which of the carboxylic acids A–E is the strongest?

    A HCOOH
    B CH_3COOH
    C CH_3CH_2COOH
    D $CH_3(CH_2)_2COOH$
    E $CH_3(CH_2)_3COOH$

What is meant by a Brønsted–Lowry acid?

2

OH

HOOC CH_2OH

With how many moles of sodium hydroxide would 0.1 mol of this compound react?

    A 0.05
    B 0.1
    C 0.2
    D 0.3
    E 0.4

Place the following in order of increasing acidic strength: phenol, carboxylic acid, alcohol.

3

H   H   H

H—C—C—C—O—C=O
                      H

H   H   H

When this ester is refluxed with dilute sodium hydroxide solution the products are:

    A propan-1-ol and methanal
    B propan-1-ol and sodium methanoate
    C propanoic acid and methanol
    D propan-2-ol and methanol
    E propanoic acid and sodium methanoate

Name this type of reaction.

4 In a titration, $25.0\,cm^3$ of $0.100\,mol\,dm^{-3}$ sodium hydroxide solution is titrated with $0.100\,mol\,dm^{-3}$ of the weak acid ethanedioic acid, $(COOH)_2$. The volume of ethanedioic acid (in cm^3) required for complete neutralisation is:

    A 2.50
    B 6.25
    C 12.5
    D 25.0
    E 37.5

Show your working.

5 Propanoic acid, CH_3CH_2COOH, dissociates in water according to the equation:

$$CH_3CH_2COOH + H_2O \rightleftharpoons CH_3CH_2COO^- + H_3O^+$$

In this equilibrium process, the $CH_3CH_2COO^-$ ion is acting as:

    A a Brønsted–Lowry acid
    B a catalyst
    C a Brønsted–Lowry base
    D an electron pair acceptor
    E an oxidising agent

Write an equation to show how propanoic acid reacts with sodium.

6 When an excess of a warm solution of ethanoic acid is added to a small amount of magnesium oxide the expected observation is:

    A a gas is produced that turns limewater milky
    B the white solid dissolves to form a colourless solution
    C a gas is produced that rekindles a glowing splint
    D the white solid dissolves and a gas is formed
    E a gas is produced that gives a squeaky pop with a lighted splint

Write an ionic equation for this reaction.

7 When an alkaline solution of phenol is added to a solution containing sodium nitrate(III) (sodium nitrite), dilute hydrochloric acid and phenylamine, and the mixture is maintained below 5°C, the product formed is:

    A an ester
    B an alcohol
    C an aromatic amine
    D an ester
    E an azo compound

What functional group is normally associated with the product of this reaction?

8 HOOC

COOH

When an excess of methanol is added to this carboxylic acid in the presence of a small amount of an acid catalyst the expected organic product is:

A ⁻OOC — COO⁻

B HOOC — OH

C HOOC — CH₂OH

D HOOC — COOCH₃

E H₃COOC — COOCH₃

Give a general use for esters.

9 When phenylamine, $C_6H_5NH_2$, is added to dilute hydrochloric acid the product is:

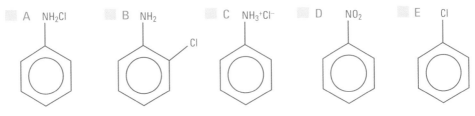

A NH_2Cl B NH_2 , Cl   C $NH_3^+Cl^-$ D NO_2 E Cl

How does phenylamine behave in this reaction?

10

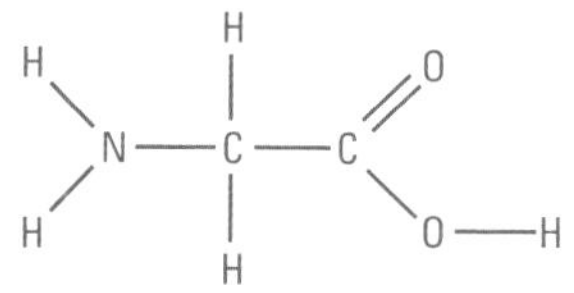

When this amino acid is in solution at pH 1.0, the dominant ionic species is:

A

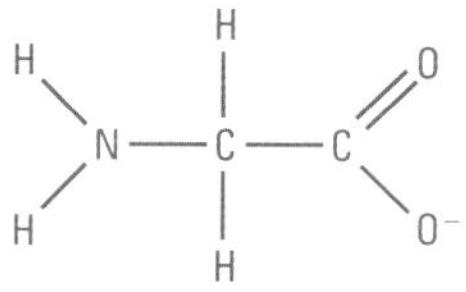

B

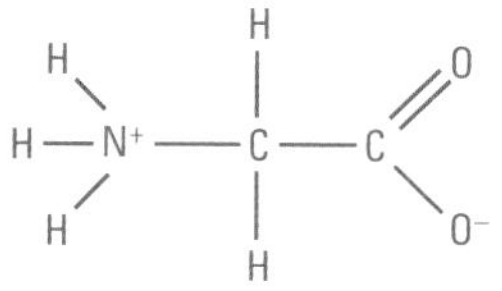

C

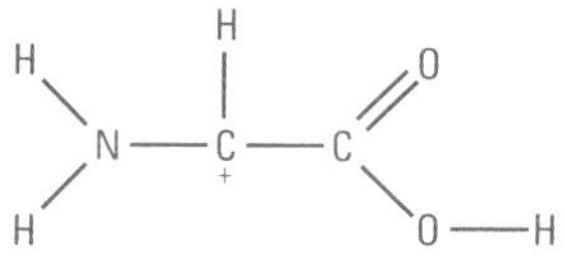

D

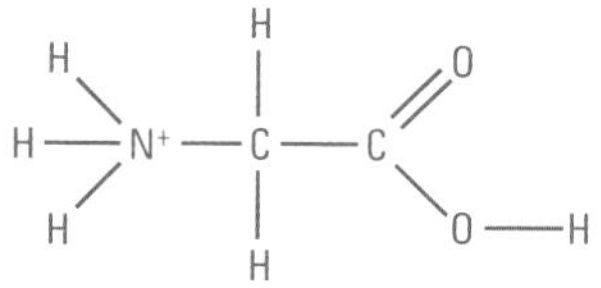

E

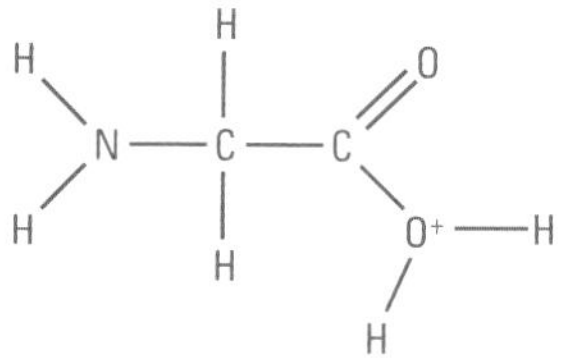

What is meant by the term 'zwitterion'?

....

....

11

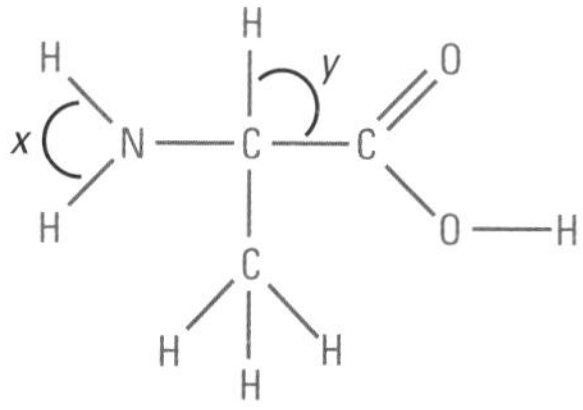

The correct values for the bond angles marked x and y in the amino acid are:

Choice	Angle x	Angle y
A	107°	109.5°
B	104.5°	104.5°
C	120°	90°
D	120°	20°
E	120°	107°

A   B   C   D   E

Is the compound featured in this question chiral?

....

....

12 When aqueous solutions containing methylamine, CH_3NH_2, and methanoic acid, HCOOH, are mixed, relevant equations include:

(1) $CH_3NH_2 + HCOOH \longrightarrow CH_3NHCOH + H_2O$

(2) $CH_3NH_2 + H_3O^+ \longrightarrow CH_3NH_3^+ + H_2O$

(3) $2HCOOH \longrightarrow (HCO)_2O + H_2O$

(4) $H_3O^+ + OH^- \longrightarrow 2H_2O$

     A   B   C   D   E

Write an equation for the reaction between methylamine and dilute hydrochloric acid.

....

....

13 The ester formed from the reaction between ethanol and methanoic acid in the presence of an acid catalyst will give which of the following positive test results?

(1) hydrogen gas is formed when sodium metal is added

(2) a white precipitate forms when warmed with silver(I) nitrate solution

(3) fizzing occurs when sodium carbonate is added

(4) a silver mirror forms with Tollens' reagent

     A   B   C   D   E

Write an equation for this reaction.

....

....

14 When treated with a cold solution of sodium nitrate(III) in dilute hydrochloric acid, followed by addition to an alkaline solution of phenol, which of the following amines form azo dyes?

(1) 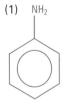   (2)    (3) 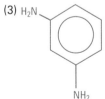   (4)

     A   B   C   D   E

Write an equation for the reaction between sodium nitrate(III) and dilute hydrochloric acid.

....

....

15 True statements about this molecule (cyclohexylamine) include:

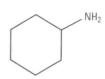

(1) it could form an amide when heated with ethanoic acid
(2) it will be neutralised by dilute hydrochloric acid
(3) in solution it will have a pH greater than 7
(4) it is an aromatic amine

    A   B   C   D   E

What would be observed when cyclohexylamine is gradually added to an aqueous solution containing copper(II) ions until it is in excess?

....

....

....

16 True statements about a solution of 1.0 mol dm^{-3} ethanoic acid, CH_3COOH, include:

(1) adding magnesium ribbon to the solution will result in a gas being formed
(2) the concentration of ethanoate ions in solution is much lower than 1.0 mol dm^{-3}
(3) the pH of the solution will increase on adding solid sodium ethanoate, CH_3COONa
(4) the pH of the solution will be approximately 1

    A   B   C   D   E

Write an equation to show how ethanoic acid dissociates in water.

....

....

17 Reaction between which of the following results in the formation of a condensation polymer?

(1) $HOOC-C_6H_4-COOH$ and $H_2N-C_6H_4-NH_2$
(2) $(COOH)_2$ and $H_2N-(CH_2)_2-NH_2$
(3) $HOOC-C_6H_4-COOH$ and $HO-(CH_2)_2-OH$
(4) CH_3COOH and $CH_3(CH_2)_2-NH_2$

    A   B   C   D   E

Name an addition polymer.

....

....

18 Which of the following are chiral?

(1)

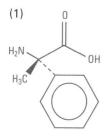

(2)

(3)

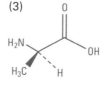

(4)

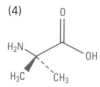

    A   B   C   D   E

What is the essential feature of a chiral molecule?

Spectroscopy

When answering the questions on spectroscopy, you may need to refer to the correlation data below.

Infrared data		NMR data	
Bond	Vibrational frequency/cm^{-1}	Type of proton	Chemical shift, δ/ppm
C–H in alkanes	2850–2960	CH$_3$–C–	0.9
C–C	750–1100	CH$_3$–C=C	1.6
C=C	1620–1680	C–CH$_2$–C	1.4
C–O	1000–1300	CH$_2$=C	4.7
C=O	1680–1750	H–phenyl	7.3
C≡N	2210–2260	CH$_3$–	2.2
O–H in hydrogen-bonded alcohols	3230–3550 (broad absorption)	CH$_3$–C=O	2.1
C–N in amines	1180–1360	CH$_3$–O–	3.3
C–Cl	600–800	CH$_3$–O–CO	3.7
C–Br	500–600	–C–CH$_2$–Br	3.5

1

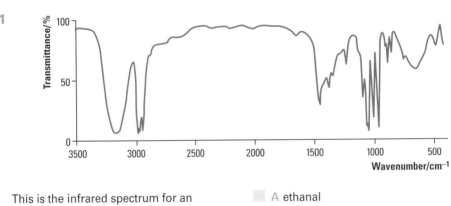

This is the infrared spectrum for an organic compound. Using the correlation data, the compound can be identified as:

A ethanal

B propan-1-ol

C bromoethane

D methanoic acid

E cyclohexene

What would be the main absorptions if the compound were propanone?

2 In the infrared region of the electro-magnetic spectrum, which of the modes A–E is responsible for an absorption of energy?

- A electronic transitions in atoms
- B nuclear transitions
- C molecular rotations
- D electronic transitions in molecules
- E molecular vibrations

Why is a nitrogen molecule, N_2, not able to absorb in the infrared region?

3

OH

CH$_3$

If this molecule were placed in a mass spectrometer, the mass of the parent ion would be:
(r.a.m. C = 12, H = 1, O = 16)

- A 98
- B 104
- C 106
- D 108
- E 114

Show your working.

4 With reference to the table, the quantities measured on the x and y axes on a typical mass spectrum are:

Choice	x-axis	y-axis
A	Density	Abundance
B	Charge density	Transmittance
C	Mass-to-charge ratio	Relative abundance
D	Mass	Relative abundance
E	Boiling point	Transmittance

A   B   C   D   E

What is meant by the term 'parent ion'?

5 Bromine has two isotopes (masses 79 and 81) in approximately equal abundance. How many peaks are expected in the molecular ion region when a sample of dibromomethane, CH_2Br_2, is placed in a mass spectrometer?

- A 1
- B 2
- C 3
- D 4
- E 5

For dibromomethane, CH_2Br_2, what are the expected height ratios of the peaks of the molecular ions consisting of two bromine atoms per molecular ion?

6 What is the height ratio of the molecular ion peaks when a sample of dichloroethane is placed into a mass spectrometer?
(r.a.m. C = 12, H = 1; isotopic abundance ^{35}Cl = 75%, ^{37}Cl = 25%)

Show your working.

    A 1:1
    B 3:1
    C 1:2:1
    D 1:3:3:1
    E 9:6:1

7 The NMR spectrum below could have been produced by:

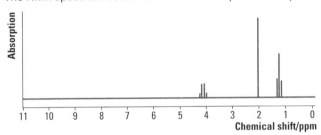

    A ethanol
    B chloroethane
    C ethyl ethanoate
    D butan-2-ol
    E methyl propanoate

What structural feature in a molecule gives rise to a triplet in the NMR spectrum?

8 Which of compounds A–E could have produced the mass spectrum below?
(r.a.m. C = 12, H = 1, O = 16)

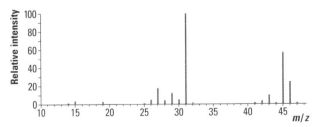

    A propanone
    B propanal
    C ethanal
    D ethanol
    E ethyl ethanoate

Why do organic compounds produce many peaks when analysed in a mass spectrometer?

9 Compound X was found to contain 87.8% C and 12.2% H.
Which of A–E could be Compound X?
(r.a.m. C = 12, H = 1)

A C_6H_{12}
B C_6H_{14}
C C_6H_{10}
D C_6H_8
E C_6H_6

Show your working.

....

....

....

10
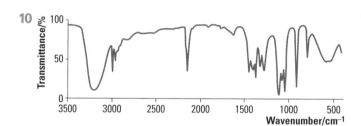

This is the infrared spectrum for the compound of structure:

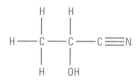

When the compound is boiled with dilute hydrochloric acid, which of the changes to the spectrum A–E takes place?

A a new absorption appears at about $1710\,\text{cm}^{-1}$
B the absorption at $2200\,\text{cm}^{-1}$ disappears
C no change is observed
D the broad absorption at $3400\,\text{cm}^{-1}$ disappears
E the absorption at $2200\,\text{cm}^{-1}$ becomes larger

What type of chemical reaction takes place?

....

....

Instructions for answering questions 11–15:

A 1, 2 and 3 only are correct
B 1 and 3 only are correct
C 2 and 4 only are correct
D 4 only is correct
E some other response

11 When samples of *n*-butane and methylpropane are analysed separately the expected spectral differences include:
(1) the NMR spectra would be identical
(2) all peaks in the mass spectra would be identical
(3) all absorptions in the infrared would disappear if D_2O were added to each compound
(4) the infrared spectra would differ

A   B   C   D   E

Which of the compounds would have the higher boiling point, and why?

....

....

....

12 In a low-resolution NMR spectrum for the ester methyl propanoate there would be:

(1) one absorption only

(2) two absorptions

(3) three absorptions of relative integral areas 3:2:3 with respect to the chemical shift axis

(4) relative integral areas of 1:1

| A | B | C | D | E |

How many proton environments does 2-chlorobutane possess?

....

....

13 Tetramethylsilane is used as a reference compound in NMR spectroscopy because:

(1) it is unreactive

(2) it has 12 equivalent protons

(3) it has a low boiling point

(4) it is colourless

| A | B | C | D | E |

What is the chemical formula for tetramethylsilane?

....

....

14

Correct statements about the compound that produced this mass spectrum include:

(1) the relative mass of the parent ion is 43

(2) the peak at 15 may be due to a methyl group, $-CH_3$

(3) there are probably more than five carbon atoms in the compound

(4) the relative mass of the parent ion is 60

| A | B | C | D | E |

What is responsible for the small peak at m/z 61?

....

....

15

H₃C — O — (hexagonal ring structure)

(r.a.m. C = 12, H = 1, O = 16)

True statements about this compound include:

(1) four peaks are expected in the low-resolution NMR spectrum
(2) the relative mass of the parent ion is 102
(3) a peak of mass/charge ratio 31 is expected in the mass spectrum
(4) an absorption in the range 3000–3300 cm⁻¹ is expected in the infrared spectrum

  A   B   C   D   E

To which organic family does this compound belong?

....

....

16 The number of proton environments in the molecule below is: A 1
                                                                        B 2
                                                                        C 3
                                                                        D 4
                                                                        E 5

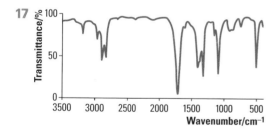

How many peaks will there be in the spectrum if D₂O is added before the NMR spectrum is recorded?

....

....

17

(two infrared spectra: left and right, axes Transmittance/% 0–100 vs Wavenumber/cm⁻¹ from 3500 to 500)

The left-hand infrared spectrum was obtained at the beginning of a reaction; the right-hand spectrum was obtained at the end. The reaction could have been:

  A hydrolysis of ethyl ethanoate
  B oxidation of ethanal
  C hydration of ethene
  D reduction of propanone
  E nitration of benzene

Name the region in an infrared spectrum that is below 1500 cm⁻¹.

....

....

18 The appearance of the high-resolution NMR spectrum of the compound below is best
described as:

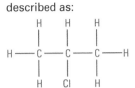

    A one singlet absorption

    B two absorptions, both singlets

    C two absorptions, one singlet and one multiplet

    D two absorptions, one doublet and one multiplet

    E three absorptions, a singlet and two doublets

How many proton environments are there in propyl propanoate?

....

....

General questions

Questions 1–5 are concerned
with the following reaction
mechanisms:

A nucleophilic addition
B electrophilic addition
C radical substitution
D nucleophilic substitution
E electrophilic substitution

1

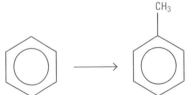

The mechanism for this
chemical transformation is:

  A
  B
  C
  D
  E

What reagents are needed for this transformation to occur?

....

....

2

CH₃

The mechanism for this
chemical transformation is:

  A
  B
  C
  D
  E

What reagents are needed for this transformation to occur?

....

....

3

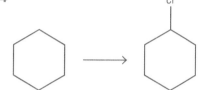

The mechanism for this chemical transformation is:

◻ A   ◻ B   ◻ C   ◻ D   ◻ E

What reagents are needed for this transformation to occur?

....

....

4

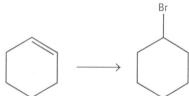

The mechanism for this chemical transformation is:

◻ A
◻ B
◻ C
◻ D
◻ E

What reagents are needed for this transformation to occur?

....

....

5

The mechanism for this chemical transformation is:

◻ A
◻ B
◻ C
◻ D
◻ E

What reagents are needed for this transformation to occur?

....

....

6

C_2H_5 C_2H_5 C_2H_5

C_2H_5 C_2H_5 C_2H_5

This polymer can be produced by polymerising:

◻ A but-2-ene
◻ B chloroethene
◻ C but-1-ene
◻ D ethene
◻ E hex-3-ene

Name this type of polymer.

....

....

7

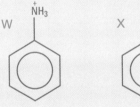

This chemical change requires:

A chlorobenzene, $AlCl_3$; heat under reflux

B phenylamine, sodium nitrate(III), dilute hydrochloric acid; temperature below 5°C

C tin in concentrated hydrochloric acid; heat under reflux

D phenol in NaOH; temperature below 5°C

E concentrated nitric acid, concentrated sulphuric acid; temperature below 50°C

Give a use for the product of this reaction.

Question 8 relates to the following molecules:

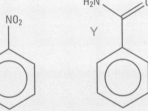

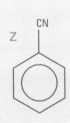

8 Species W was detected in aqueous solution. Its presence could have been caused by:

A heating benzene with ammonia at high pressure

B adding compound X to dilute hydrochloric acid

C adding dilute sulphuric acid to phenylamine

D warming compound Y with dilute sodium hydroxide solution

E reducing compound Z with hydrogen and a nickel catalyst at 150°C

Write an equation to show the reaction between the ion featured in this question ($C_6H_5NH_3^+$) and hydroxide ions.

9 Which of reactions A–E produces a chiral product?

    A CH_3CH_2CHO, $Na_2Cr_2O_7$, H^+; heat under reflux
    B $C_6H_5CH_2Br$, NaOH(aq); heat under reflux
    C HCHO, HCN with a trace of KCN
    D acid hydrolysis of $C_6H_5COOCH_2CH_3$
    E addition of HBr to $C_6H_5CH=CH_2$

What is the meaning of the symbols (+) and (–) when placed in front of the name of a chiral compound?

....

....

....

....

10 Which of A–E is *not* a nucleophile?

    A BF_3 B CO   C NH_3 D Cl^- E CH_3NH_2

Write an equation for the reaction between ethanolic ammonia and bromoethane.

....

....

Instructions for answering questions 11–15:

    A 1, 2 and 3 only are correct
    B 1 and 3 only are correct
    C 2 and 4 only are correct
    D 4 only is correct
    E some other response

11 On the addition of a few drops of 2,4-dinitrophenylhydrazine, which of the following would *not* produce an orange precipitate?
(1) ethanal
(2) ethanoic acid
(3) propanone
(4) ethyl ethanoate   A   B   C   D   E

What further procedure would result in the identification of the original carbonyl compound?

....

....

....

....

12 True statements about this molecule include:

(1) it can be polymerised under certain conditions

(2) it decolorises bromine water

(3) it forms a chiral compound when treated with hydrogen cyanide in trace KCN

(4) it forms a silver mirror with ammoniacal silver(I) nitrate (Tollens' reagent)

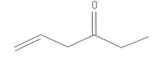

     A   B   C   D   E

Is the compound expected to react with 2,4-dinitrophenylhydrazine?

....

....

13

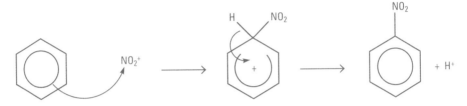

True statements about this mechanism include:

(1) it is a nucleophilic substitution

(2) the NO_2^+ ion in the first step behaves as an electrophile

(3) NO_2^+ is called a nitrate(v) ion

(4) the pair of electrons in the first stage originates from the pi-system on the benzene ring

     A   B   C   D   E

Suggest a reason why the intermediate formed as a result of the first step loses a proton.

....

....

....

....

14 In the high-resolution NMR spectrum of this compound, the peaks expected include:

(1) a singlet

(2) a doublet

(3) a triplet

(4) a quartet

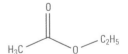

     A   B   C   D   E

How many proton environments are present in propyl methanoate?

....

....

Question 15 concerns the following compounds:

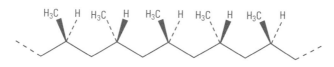

X

$$HOOC - \underset{\underset{CH_3}{|}}{\overset{\overset{H}{|}}{C}} - NH_2$$

Y

$$HOOC - \underset{\underset{CH_3}{|}}{\overset{\overset{H}{|}}{C}} - \overset{+}{N}H_3$$

Z

$$^-OOC - \underset{\underset{CH_3}{|}}{\overset{\overset{H}{|}}{C}} - NH_2$$

15 When substance X is dissolved in dilute hydrochloric acid, which of the following statements are true?

(1) the compound remains in its molecular form
(2) positive ions form, which have structure Y
(3) negative ions form, which have the structure Z
(4) a neutralisation reaction takes place

           A   B   C   D   E

To which class of organic compounds does the molecule X belong?

....

....

16

H_3C H H_3C H H_3C H H_3C H H_3C H

This polymer is called:

- A isotactic polybut-2-ene
- B atactic polypropene
- C syndiotactic polybut-1-ene
- D syndiotactic polypropene
- E atactic polybut-2-ene

What is the empirical formula of this polymer?

....

....

Questions 17 and 18 concern the following reaction scheme:

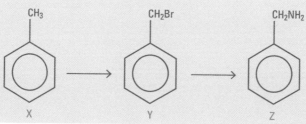

CH_3 CH_2Br CH_2NH_2

X   Y   Z

17 The reagents and conditions needed for the conversion of compound X into compound Y are:

- A Br_2, $AlBr_3$; heat under reflux
- B $KBr(aq)$; warm
- C HBr; room temperature
- D Br_2; ultraviolet light
- E CH_3Br, $FeBr_3$; heat under reflux

Name compound X.

....

....

18 The type of reaction taking place when compound Y is converted into compound Z is:

- A an addition
- B an oxidation
- C a substitution
- D a reduction
- E a hydrolysis

What reagents are needed to convert compound X into compound Z?

....

....

Transition metal chemistry

Transition metals and complexes

Instructions for answering questions 1–6:

A 1, 2 and 3 only are correct
B 1 and 3 only are correct
C 2 and 4 only are correct
D 4 only is correct
E some other response

1 True statements about chromium (atomic number 24) include:
(1) it has an electronic configuration of $1s^2, 2s^2, 2p^6, 3s^2, 3p^6, 4s^2, 3d^4$
(2) its expected maximum oxidation state is +6 or VI
(3) metallic chromium is likely to display catalytic behaviour
(4) a Cr^{3+} ion has an electronic configuration of $1s^2, 2s^2, 2p^6, 3s^2, 3p^6, 4s^2, 3d^1$

    A   B   C   D   E

Write an equation to show chromium reacting with chlorine to form chromium(III) chloride.

2 In which of the following does the transition metal have the same oxidation number as chromium in K_2CrO_4?
(1) K_2MnO_4
(2) $CuCl_2$
(3) CrO_3
(4) CoF_3

    A   B   C   D   E

Is the chromium in K_2CrO_4 likely to react by donating or accepting electrons? Explain your answer.

3 True statements about the complex ion of formula $[Ni(H_2O)_6]^{2+}$ include:
(1) nickel has the oxidation number +2
(2) the complex is pale green
(3) the complex is octahedral
(4) the ion migrates towards the anode during electrolysis

    A   B   C   D   E

What is the coordination number of nickel in $[Ni(H_2O)_6]^{2+}$?

4 Correct statements about the addition of potassium thiocyanate solution, KSCN(aq), to an aqueous solution containing iron(III) ions include:
(1) a redox reaction takes place
(2) a dark red solution is observed
(3) the potassium ion acts as a ligand in the reaction
(4) the ion $[Fe(SCN)(H_2O)_5]^{2+}$ is formed

    A   B   C   D   E

What is the oxidation number of iron in $[Fe(SCN)(H_2O)_5]^{2+}$?

....

....

5 Which of the following square planar transition-metal complex ions display geometric isomerism?
(1) $[NiCl_2(NH_3)_2]$
(2) $[Cu(H_2O)_4]^{2+}$
(3) $[Pt(NH_3)_2Cl_2]$
(4) $[PdCl_4]^{2-}$

    A   B   C   D   E

Is it possible for two geometrically related isomers to have different chemical properties?

....

....

6 Which of the following species are likely to behave as ligands?
(1) Cl^-
(2) CH_3NH_2
(3) CO
(4) NH_4^+

    A   B   C   D   E

Is the molecule BF_3 expected to act as a ligand?

....

....

7 When sodium hydroxide solution is added to separate solutions containing iron(II) and iron(III) ions, what are the expected colours of the precipitates?

Choice	Iron(II)	Iron(III)
A	White	Yellow
B	Yellow	Mauve
C	Green	Brown
D	Orange	Blue
E	Blue	Green

    A   B   C   D   E

Name the precipitates formed when sodium hydroxide solution reacts with iron(II) and iron(III) ions.

....

....

8 Which of A–E is *not* a property normally associated with transition metals?

   A high tensile strength
   B complex formation
   C coloured compounds
   D catalytic behaviour
   E low melting temperatures

Is it true that transition metals often show more than one oxidation state in their compounds?

....

....

9 When a solution of ammonia is added dropwise to a solution containing copper(II) ions, until in excess:

   A fizzing occurs and a dark-blue precipitate forms
   B a pale-blue precipitate is formed that dissolves to form a dark-blue solution
   C a pink precipitate forms that dissolves to form a blue solution
   D a yellow solution forms that darkens when exposed to air
   E a green solution forms that turns yellow on leaving in air

Give the types of reaction involved when ammonia is added dropwise to a solution containing copper(II) ions.

....

....

10 The transition metal complex ion that produced the visible absorption spectrum below is:

   A red
   B colourless
   C blue
   D green
   E purple

Describe briefly how a transition metal ion in an octahedral complex interacts with visible light.

....

....

....

....

....

11 The nature of the bonding between a ligand and a transition metal within a transition metal complex is:

- A a hydrogen bond
- B an ionic interaction
- C a dative bond
- D a van der Waals interaction
- E a non-polar covalent bond

Write the formula for the tetrahedral complex in which a central nickel(II) ion bonds to four cyanide ligands, CN^-.

....

....

12 Which of metals A–E is *not* likely to form a coloured chloride?

- A nickel
- B vanadium
- C copper
- D cobalt
- E zinc

Write an ionic equation for the reaction between nickel(II) chloride solution and silver(I) nitrate solution.

....

....

Questions 13–16 are concerned with the following analysis:

A 3.500 g sample of iron(II) sulphate, $FeSO_4$, was found to be contaminated with iron(III) oxide. The sample was dissolved in dilute sulphuric acid and made up to $250.0 \, cm^3$ in a volumetric flask. A $25.00 \, cm^3$ sample was then withdrawn, placed in a conical flask and titrated with $0.0200 \, mol \, dm^{-3}$ potassium manganate(VII) solution. Complete reaction required $22.20 \, cm^3$ of potassium manganate(VII) solution. The equation for the reaction is:

$$5Fe^{2+}(aq) + MnO_4^-(aq) + 8H^+(aq) \longrightarrow 5Fe^{3+}(aq) + 4H_2O(l) + Mn^{x+}(aq)$$

(r.a.m. Fe = 56, S = 32, O = 16)

---

13 With reference to the table, choose a correct statement about the oxidation number changes, if any, in this reaction.

Choice	Manganese	Iron
A	−1 to +2	+2 to +3
B	+4 to +1	+2 to 0
C	+7 to +2	+2 to +3
D	+6 to +3	+2 to +3
E	No change	No change

A   B   C   D   E

Name the chemical process that has taken place on the manganate(VII) ion in this reaction.

....

....

14 The value of x in the ion $Mn^{x+}(aq)$ in this reaction is:

                A 0   B 1   C 2   D 3   E 4

Show your working.

....

....

....

15 The colour change seen at the end point of the titration is:

    A pale blue to green
    B colourless to pale pink
    C colourless to green
    D orange to colourless
    E pale pink to colourless

Explain why an indicator is not necessary in a typical redox titration using potassium manganate(VII).

....

....

....

16 The percentage by mass of iron(II) sulphate in the original sample was:

    A 7.10
    B 19.0
    C 36.1
    D 65.2
    E 96.4

Show your working.

....

....

....

....

....

17 The complex that can exhibit optical isomerism is:

    A $[Ni(NH_3)_2Br_2]$
    B $Cr(H_2O)_6Cl_3$
    C $[CuCl_4]^{2-}$
    D $[Co(H_2N-CH_2CH_2-NH_2)_3]^{3+}$
    E $[Ag(NH_3)_2]^+$

What are optical isomers?

....

....

18 In an experiment, a 0.1 mol dm⁻³ solution of hydrochloric acid was added to 10 cm³ of a solution that was 0.1 mol dm⁻³ with respect to chromium(III) ions. As the volume of hydrochloric acid was varied, the absorption of light at a particular wavelength was monitored. The following graph was obtained:

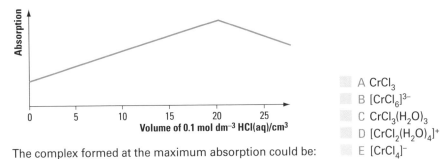

A $CrCl_3$
B $[CrCl_6]^{3-}$
C $CrCl_3(H_2O)_3$
D $[CrCl_2(H_2O)_4]^+$
E $[CrCl_4]^-$

The complex formed at the maximum absorption could be:

Show your working.

Redox chemistry and catalysis

Questions 1–5 are concerned with the following equilibria and their associated standard electrode potentials:

A $Ag^+(aq) + e^- \rightleftharpoons Ag(s)$ $E^\ominus = +0.80\,V$
B $Fe^{3+}(aq) + e^- \rightleftharpoons Fe^{2+}(aq)$ $E^\ominus = +0.77\,V$
C $Cl_2(aq) + 2e^- \rightleftharpoons 2Cl^-(aq)$ $E^\ominus = +1.36\,V$
D $H^+(aq) + e^- \rightleftharpoons \frac{1}{2}H_2(g)$ $E^\ominus = 0.00\,V$
E $I_2(aq) + 2e^- \rightleftharpoons 2I^-(aq)$ $E^\ominus = +0.54\,V$

1 Which of A–E contains the strongest oxidising agent?

A   B   C   D   E

What is the link between oxidising power and the magnitude of the electrode potential?

2 Which of A–E is used as the standard against which all other electrode potentials are compared?

A   B   C   D   E

Give a hazard associated with the use of this particular reference electrode.

3 Which of A–E contains the species that is able to reduce copper(II) ions in solution?

$Cu^{2+}(aq) + 2e^- \rightleftharpoons Cu(s)$ $E^\ominus = +0.34\,V$

A   B   C   D   E

What is the link, if any, between electrode potential and reaction rate?

4 Which of A–E contains the strongest reducing agent?

A   B   C   D   E

Does sodium behave as a reducing agent or as an oxidising agent? Explain your answer.

5 Which of A–E contains the species that may be capable of oxidising chromium(III) ions to dichromate(VI) ions in acidic solution?

$Cr_2O_7^{2-}(aq) + 14H^+(aq) + 6e^- \rightleftharpoons 2Cr^{3+}(aq) + 7H_2O(l)$ $E^\ominus = +1.33\,V$

A   B   C   D   E

How many moles of iodide ions, I^-, will 1 mol of dichromate(VI) ions oxidise?

6 Consider the reaction:

$2Cu^+(aq) \longrightarrow Cu(s) + Cu^{2+}(aq)$

$\begin{pmatrix} Cu^{2+}(aq) + e^- \rightleftharpoons Cu^+(aq) & E^\ominus = +0.15\,V \\ Cu^+(aq) + e^- \rightleftharpoons Cu(s) & E^\ominus = +0.52\,V \end{pmatrix}$

What is the standard electrode potential (in volts) for this reaction?

A +0.88
B −0.72
C −0.68
D +0.37
E +0.74

What is the electrode potential for the following process?

$Cu(s) + Cu^{2+}(aq) \longrightarrow 2Cu^+(aq)$

7 The compound containing the element in the highest positive oxidation state is:

A $Mg(NO_3)_2$
B Al_2Cl_6
C $KMnO_4$
D $KClO_4$
E OsO_4

Compounds possessing a metal in a high positive oxidation state are likely to behave as what type of reagent?

8 In which of reactions A–E is chlorine oxidised?

A $ClO_3^- + 6H^+ + 5e^- \longrightarrow \frac{1}{2}Cl_2 + 3H_2O$
B $2Na(s) + Cl_2(g) \longrightarrow 2NaCl(s)$
C $F_2(g) + 2Cl^-(aq) \longrightarrow Cl_2(aq) + 2F^-(aq)$
D $\frac{1}{2}Cl_2 + e^- \longrightarrow Cl^-$
E $HOCl + H^+ + e^- \longrightarrow \frac{1}{2}Cl_2 + H_2O$

Write a half-equation showing the reduction of magnesium ions to magnesium atoms.

....

....

9

Equilibrium	Electrode potential/V
$I_2(aq) + 2e^- \rightleftharpoons 2I^-(aq)$	+0.54
$Ni^{2+}(aq) + 2e^- \rightleftharpoons Ni(s)$	−0.25
$Fe^{3+}(aq) + e^- \rightleftharpoons Fe^{2+}(aq)$	+0.77
$S_2O_8^{2-}(aq) + 2e^- \rightleftharpoons 2SO_4^{2-}(aq)$	+2.01

Consider the following redox reaction:

$$S_2O_8^{2-}(aq) + 2I^-(aq) \longrightarrow 2SO_4^{2-}(aq) + I_2(aq)$$

Using the electrode potential data given, predict which of ions A–E can catalyse this reaction.

A Fe^{2+} only
B Fe^{3+} and Ni^{2+}
C Ni^{2+} and Fe^{2+}
D Fe^{2+} and Fe^{3+}
E Fe^{3+} only

Suggest why the reaction between $S_2O_8^{2-}$ ions and I^- ions is slow under normal conditions.
....

....

....

....

10 Consider the reaction:

$$Cr_2O_7^{2-}(aq) + 14H^+(aq) + 6Cl^-(aq) \longrightarrow 2Cr^{3+}(aq) + 7H_2O(l) + 3Cl_2(aq)$$

$\begin{pmatrix} Cl_2(aq) + 2e^- \rightleftharpoons 2Cl^-(aq) \quad E^\oplus = +1.36\,V \\ Cr_2O_7^{2-}(aq) + 14H^+(aq) + 6e^- \rightleftharpoons 2Cr^{3+}(aq) + 7H_2O(l) \quad E^\oplus = +1.33\,V \end{pmatrix}$

• The electrode potential (volts) for this reaction is:

A +2.69
B +0.03
C +2.75
D −0.03
E −2.75

What could be done to the following process to make the forward reaction more likely to occur?

$$Cr_2O_7^{2-}(aq) + 14H^+(aq) + 6e^- \rightleftharpoons 2Cr^{3+}(aq) + 7H_2O(l)$$

....

....

11 When measuring the standard electrode potential for zinc metal using a hydrogen electrode, which of conditions A–E is *not* used?

A 1 mol dm^{-3} $Zn^{2+}(aq)$
B 298 K
C a high-resistance voltmeter
D 1 mol dm^{-3} H_2SO_4
E hydrogen gas at 1 atm pressure

Write an equation to show the process occurring at the negative electrode in this cell.

....

....

Instructions for answering questions 12–15:

A 1, 2 and 3 only are correct
B 1 and 3 only are correct
C 2 and 4 only are correct
D 4 only is correct
E some other response

12 Consider the reaction:

$$N_2(g) + 3H_2(g) \rightleftharpoons 2NH_3(g)$$

Iron is used in this process. True statements about its role include:

(1) it provides a surface on which the gas molecules can react
(2) it bonds very weakly to both hydrogen and nitrogen molecules
(3) it acts as a heterogeneous catalyst
(4) it bonds strongly to the ammonia molecules formed

A   B   C   D   E

The rate-determining step for this process involves the conversion of a nitrogen molecule into nitrogen atoms. Explain why you would expect this to be the case.

....

....

....

13 Consider the reaction:

$$Hg^{2+}(aq) + 2e^- \rightleftharpoons Hg(l) \quad E^\ominus = +0.85 \text{ V}$$
$$(H^+(aq) + e^- \rightleftharpoons \tfrac{1}{2}H_2(g) \quad E^\ominus = 0.00 \text{ V})$$

Correct statements regarding the standard electrode potential for mercury include:

(1) mercury(II) ions have a lower tendency to gain electrons compared with hydrogen ions
(2) hydrogen gas is a more powerful reducing agent than mercury
(3) the electrode potential for $2Hg^{2+}(aq) + 4e^- \rightleftharpoons 2Hg(l)$ is +1.70 V
(4) mercury should react with acids to form $Hg^{2+}(aq)$ ions

A   B   C   D   E

Write an equation for the spontaneous reaction.

....

....

14 Which of the following features an element that disproportionates?

(1) $Cl_2 + H_2O \longrightarrow HOCl + HCl$

(2) $2Cu^+ \longrightarrow Cu + Cu^{2+}$

(3) $3ClO^- \longrightarrow 2Cl^- + ClO_3^-$

(4) $MnO_4^- + 8H^+ + 5e^- \longrightarrow Mn^{2+} + 4H_2O$

        ▨ A   ▨ B   ▨ C   ▨ D   ▨ E

Define disproportionation.

....

....

15 Which of the following would *not* result in a different electrode potential being measured when determining the standard electrode potential for nickel using a hydrogen electrode?

(1) increasing the concentration of nickel(II) ions to $2.0\,mol\,dm^{-3}$

(2) using a different soluble nickel salt of the same concentration

(3) decreasing the temperature

(4) lowering the nickel further into the nickel(II) solution so that more solution makes contact with the metal surface

        ▨ A   ▨ B   ▨ C   ▨ D   ▨ E

Write an equation to describe the oxidation of nickel to nickel(II).

....

....

Questions 16–18 are concerned with the following analysis:

    A coin (assumed to be an alloy of nickel and copper only) of mass 2.500 g was completely dissolved in concentrated nitric(V) acid. The solution was made up to $250.0\,cm^3$ in a volumetric flask; $25.00\,cm^3$ were withdrawn and placed in a conical flask. Excess potassium iodide was then added and the liberated iodine was titrated with $0.0500\,mol\,dm^{-3}$ sodium thiosulphate solution. It was found that $35.20\,cm^3$ of sodium thiosulphate was required for complete reaction.

Relevant chemical equations:

$Cu(s) + 4HNO_3(l) \longrightarrow Cu(NO_3)_2(aq) + 2NO_2(g) + 2H_2O(l)$

$2Cu^{2+}(aq) + 4I^-(aq) \longrightarrow 2CuI(s) + I_2(aq)$

$2Na_2S_2O_3(aq) + I_2(aq) \longrightarrow Na_2S_4O_6(aq) + 2NaI(aq)$

$\begin{pmatrix} NO_3^-(aq) + 2H^+(aq) + e^- \rightleftharpoons NO_2(g) + H_2O(l) & E^\ominus = +0.81\,V \\ Cu^{2+}(aq) + 2e^- \rightleftharpoons Cu(s) & E^\ominus = +0.34\,V \end{pmatrix}$

(r.a.m. Cu = 63.5)

16

Choice	Change in oxidation number of nitrogen	Change in oxidation number of copper
A	0 to +5	0 to +1
B	+2 to +4	+1 to 0
C	+5 to +4	+2 to 0
D	+4 to 0	0 to +1
E	+5 to +4	0 to +2

When copper reacts with concentrated nitric acid, the letter that represents the changes in oxidation number of nitrogen and copper is:

    A   B   C   D   E

Show your working.

17 Consider the reaction:

$Cu(s) + 2NO_3^-(aq) + 4H^+(aq) \longrightarrow Cu^{2+}(aq) + 2NO_2(g) + 2H_2O(l)$

The electrode potential (in volts) for this reaction is:

    A +1.15   B +1.28   C +0.47   D −1.15   E −0.47

Show your working.

18 The total amount (moles) of copper(II) ions formed when the coin dissolved in the concentrated nitric acid was:

    A 1.76×10^{-2}
    B 8.80×10^{-3}
    C 3.52×10^{-3}
    D 8.80×10^{-4}
    E 3.52×10^{-2}

Show your working.

The chemistry of selected transition metals

Questions 1–5 are concerned with the following transition metal compounds:

A $CoCl_2$ B CuCl   C $FeSO_4$ D Na_2CrO_4 E NH_4VO_3

1 Which of compounds A–E, when in solution, forms an orange solution on the addition of dilute sulphuric acid?

     A   B   C   D   E

Give the formula of the anion formed in the process.

....

....

2 Which of compounds A–E is likely to disproportionate when in solution?

     A   B   C   D   E

Write an ionic equation to show this disproportionation taking place.

....

....

3 Which of compounds A–E contains a transition metal in the oxidation state of +5?

     A   B   C   D   E

How is the compound expected to behave in a redox reaction?

....

....

4 Which of compounds A–E, when in solution, forms a green precipitate on the addition of aqueous sodium hydroxide?

     A   B   C   D   E

What is the formula for the precipitate formed?

....

....

5 Which of compounds A–E dissolves in water to form a pink solution?

     A   B   C   D   E

What colours of the visible spectrum is the complex absorbing?

....

....

Questions 6–10 are concerned with the following reaction scheme:

$$CrCl_3(aq) \longrightarrow Cr(OH)_3(s) \longrightarrow [Cr(OH)_6]^{3-}(aq) \longrightarrow CrO_4^{2-}(aq)$$

   W   X   Y   Z

6 Compound W can be converted into compound X by:

  A acidified potassium manganate(VI)
  B aqueous sodium hydroxide solution
  C dilute sulphuric acid
  D zinc in dilute sulphuric acid
  E magnesium ribbon

Is the conversion of compound W into X oxidation, reduction or neither? Explain your answer.

....

....

7 The colour and shape of the complex ion $[Cr(OH)_6]^{3-}(aq)$ is:

Choice	Colour	Shape
A	Yellow	Octahedral
B	Green	Tetrahedral
C	Orange	Square planar
D	Green	Octahedral
E	Blue	Tetrahedral

  A   B   C   D   E

Is this ion likely to travel to the cathode or the anode when in aqueous solution?

....

....

8 When ion Y is converted into ion Z, the type of reaction is:

  A reduction
  B disproportionation
  C ligand substitution
  D oxidation
  E addition

Give the formula of calcium chromate(VI).

....

....

9 Ion Y can be converted into ion Z by:

  A $H_2O_2(aq)$
  B $Zn/H_2SO_4(aq)$
  C $CO_2(g)$
  D $NH_3(aq)$
  E $H_2N(CH_2)_2NH_2$

What is the oxidation state of chromium in CrO_4^{2-}?

....

....

10 The colour of ion Z is:

    A green
    B orange
    C blue
    D red
    E yellow

Write an equation to show the equilibrium that exists when ion Z is added to an acid.

....

....

Questions 11–15 are concerned with the following standard electrode potentials:

Reaction	Standard electrode potential, $E^{\ominus}$ / V
$VO_2^+(aq) + 2H^+(aq) + e^- \rightleftharpoons VO^{2+}(aq) + H_2O(l)$	+1.00
$VO^{2+}(aq) + 2H^+(aq) + e^- \rightleftharpoons V^{3+}(aq) + H_2O(l)$	+0.34
$V^{3+}(aq) + e^- \rightleftharpoons V^{2+}(aq)$	−0.26
$V^{2+}(aq) + 2e^- \rightleftharpoons V(s)$	−1.20
$Zn^{2+}(aq) + 2e^- \rightleftharpoons Zn(s)$	−0.76
$I_2(aq) + 2e^- \rightleftharpoons 2I^-(aq)$	+0.54

11 Consider the reaction:
$$2VO_2^+(aq) + 4H^+(aq) + Zn(s) \rightleftharpoons 2VO^{2+}(aq) + Zn^{2+}(aq) + 2H_2O(l)$$
The electrode potential (in volts) for this process is:

    A +1.76
    B +0.24
    C −0.24
    D +1.24
    E −1.76

Show your working. ....

....

12 When excess zinc is added to an acidified solution of vanadate(v) ions, $VO_2^+(aq)$, the final vanadium-containing product is:

    A V(s)
    B $V^{2+}(aq)$
    C $V^{3+}(aq)$
    D $VO^{2+}(aq)$
    E $VO_2^+(aq)$

Write a half-equation to show the overall conversion of the ion $VO_2^+(aq)$ into the vanadium-containing product.

....

....

13 The colours of the oxidation
states of vanadium are
represented by:

Choice	Vanadium(v)	Vanadium(IV)	Vanadium(III)	Vanadium(II)
A	Orange	Yellow	Blue	Green
B	Yellow	Blue	Green	Violet
C	Blue	Colourless	Brown	Pink
D	Violet	Green	Yellow	Red
E	Yellow	Green	Red	Blue

░ A   ░ B   ░ C   ░ D   ░ E

Write a half-equation to show the overall conversion of vanadium(IV), as $VO^{2+}(aq)$, to
vandium(II), as $V^{2+}(aq)$.

....

....

14 When iodide ions are added to a solution of acidified
vanadate(v) ions, $VO_2^+(aq)$, the final vanadium-containing
product is:

    ░ A $V(s)$
    ░ B $V^{2+}(aq)$
    ░ C $V^{3+}(aq)$
    ░ D $VO^{2+}(aq)$
    ░ E $VO_2^+(aq)$

Show your working.

....

....

....

....

....

....

....

....

15 When a piece of vanadium metal is added to a solution
containing vanadate(v) ions, $VO_2^+(aq)$, the species that
forms is:

    ░ A $V(s)$
    ░ B $V^{2+}(aq)$
    ░ C $V^{3+}(aq)$
    ░ D $VO^{2+}(aq)$
    ░ E $VO_2^+(aq)$

Give the formula of this complex ion in aqueous solution.

....

....

Questions 16–18 are concerned with the following reaction scheme, involving cobalt:

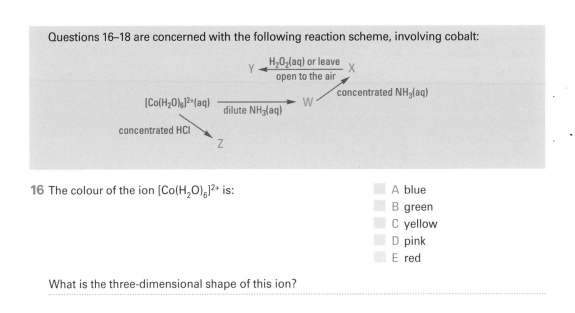

16 The colour of the ion $[Co(H_2O)_6]^{2+}$ is:

    A blue
    B green
    C yellow
    D pink
    E red

What is the three-dimensional shape of this ion?

....

....

17 The cobalt-containing species formed in the reaction are represented by:

Choice	Compound W	Compound X	Compound Y	Compound Z
A	$Co(OH)_2(H_2O)_4$	$[Co(NH_3)_6]^{2+}$	$[Co(NH_3)_6]^{3+}$	$[CoCl_4]^{2-}$
B	$[Co(NH_3)_6]^{2+}$	$[Co(NH_3)_6]^{3+}$	$[Co(OH)_6]^{3-}$	$[CoCl_6]^{3-}$
C	$Co(OH)_2(H_2O)_4$	$[Co(NH_3)_6]^{3+}$	$[Co(NH_3)_6]^{2+}$	$[CoCl_4]^{2-}$
D	$[Co(NH_3)_6]^{3+}$	$[Co(NH_3)_6]^{2+}$	Co_2O_3	$CoCl_2$
E	$Co(OH)_3(H_2O)_3$	$[Co(OH)_2(NH_3)_4]^{2+}$	CoO	$CoCl_3$

    A   B   C   D   E

What is the oxidation number of the cobalt in $[Co(NH_3)_6]Cl_3$?

....

....

18 What are the names for the reactions that takes place in the conversion of W into X and X into Y?

Choice	Conversion of W into X	Conversion of X into Y
A	Redox	Precipitation
B	Acid–base	Ligand substitution
C	Redox	Acid–base
D	Ligand substitution	Redox
E	Precipitation	Acid–base

    A   B   C   D   E

Cobalt reacts with fluorine gas to form cobalt(III) fluoride. Write an equation for this reaction.

....

....

General questions

1 The graph shows how the light absorption for a complex formed between a 0.10 mol dm^{-3} solution of transition metal X and a 0.10 mol dm^{-3} solution of a ligand Y varies as the relative volumes of X and Y are changed.

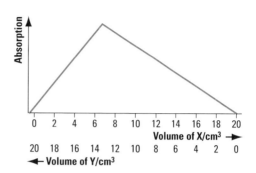

The formula of the complex formed in the experiment is:

    A X_2Y

    B XY

    C XY_2

    D X_2Y_3

    E X_3Y_2

Explain why the graph has a maximum absorption.

....

....

....

....

2 A bidentate ligand, X^{2-}, is added to a solution containing a transition metal, Y^{2+}, and an octahedral complex forms. The formula of the complex is:

    A $[YX]^{2+}$

    B $[YX_2]^{2-}$

    C $[YX]^{2-}$

    D $[YX_3]^{4-}$

    E $[YX_2]^0$

If the resulting complex were square planar shape, what would its formula be?

....

....

3 The oxidation number of chromium in the complex $[CrCl(H_2O)_5]^+$ is:

    A -1

    B 0

    C $+1$

    D $+2$

    E $+3$

What is the oxidation number of chromium in the compound CrO_3?

....

....

4 Which of complexes A–E could form geometric isomers?

A $[Cr(NH_3)_2(H_2O)_4]^{3+}$
B $PtCl_4^{2-}$
C $[CuCl_4]^{2-}$
D $[CoF_4]^-$
E $[Cr(NH_3)_6]^{3+}$

What is the oxidation number of chromium in $[Cr(NH_3)_2(H_2O)_4]^{3+}$?

5 Which of A–E does *not* behave as a ligand?

A NH_3
B I^-
C $H_2N(CH_2)_2NH_2$
D BF_3
E C_2H_4

What is a ligand?

6 Vanadate(v) ions, VO_2^+, are converted into vanadium(II) ions, V^{2+}, by:

A NaOH(aq)
B concentrated HCl
C Zn in dilute H_2SO_4
D Fe^{2+}(aq)
E $KMnO_4$(aq) in dilute H_2SO_4(aq)

Write a half-equation to show the overall conversion of vanadate(v) ions, VO_2^+, into vanadium(II) ions, V^{2+}.

7 The colour of copper(I) iodide is:

A blue
B yellow
C pink–brown
D green
E white

How many $3d$ electrons are present in copper in copper(I) iodide? (The atomic number of copper is 29.)

8 Manganese has an atomic number of 25. The electronic configuration of a manganese(II) ion is:

A $1s^2, 2s^2, 2p^6, 3s^2, 3p^6, 4s^2, 3d^5$
B $1s^2, 2s^2, 2p^6, 3s^2, 3p^6, 4s^1, 3d^4$
C $1s^2, 2s^2, 2p^6, 3s^2, 3p^6, 3d^5$
D $1s^2, 2s^2, 2p^6, 3s^2, 3p^6, 4s^2, 3d^3$
E $1s^2, 2s^2, 2p^6, 3s^2, 3p^6, 4s^2, 3d^7$

What is the oxidation number of manganese in K_2MnO_4?

9

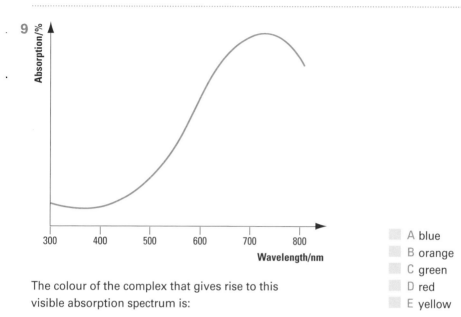

The colour of the complex that gives rise to this visible absorption spectrum is:

- A blue
- B orange
- C green
- D red
- E yellow

In a transition metal ion, how are the energies of the five $3d$ orbitals affected when ligands bond to form an octahedral complex?

10 Consider the equation:

$$2Fe^{3+}(aq) + 2I^-(aq) \longrightarrow 2Fe^{2+}(aq) + I_2(aq)$$

$$\begin{pmatrix} I_2(aq) + 2e^- \rightleftharpoons 2I^-(aq) & E^\ominus = +0.54\,V \\ Fe^{3+}(aq) + e^- \rightleftharpoons Fe^{2+}(aq) & E^\ominus = +0.77\,V \end{pmatrix}$$

The expected standard electrode potential (in volts) for this process is:

- A +1.31
- B +0.23
- C +1.00
- D −1.31
- E −0.23

Show your working.

Instructions for answering questions 11–15:

- A 1, 2 and 3 only are correct
- B 1 and 3 only are correct
- C 2 and 4 only are correct
- D 4 only is correct
- E some other response

11 Consider the equation:

$$5Fe^{2+}(aq) + MnO_4^-(aq) + 8H^+(aq) \longrightarrow 5Fe^{3+}(aq) + Mn^{2+}(aq) + 4H_2O(l)$$

True statements about this process include:

(1) Fe^{2+} is a reducing agent

(2) H^+ is a catalyst in the reaction

(3) MnO_4^- is an oxidising agent

(4) each manganate(VII) ion gains one electron

                 A   B   C   D   E

How many moles of hydrogen ions, $H^+(aq)$, react with 1 mol of manganate(VII) ions in the half-equation?

12 Transition metals that have the same oxidation number as iron in the complex $[Fe(CN)_6]^{4-}$ include those in the following ligands:

(1) VBr_3

(2) $CuBr_2$

(3) K_2MnO_4

(4) NiO A   B   C   D   E

What is the oxidation number of iron in $FeCO_3$?

13 True statements about the addition of potassium thiocyanate solution, KNCS(aq), to a solution containing iron(III) ions include:

(1) the ion $[Fe(NCS)(H_2O)_5]^{2+}(aq)$ is formed

(2) a gas is produced

(3) a blood-red solution is formed

(4) a ligand substitution process takes place

                 A   B   C   D   E

Explain why this is not a redox reaction.

14 True statements about the complex ion $[Cr(en)_3]^{3+}$ in which 'en' is the ligand $H_2N(CH_2)_2NH_2$ include:

(1) chromium has a coordination number of 3

(2) the complex is capable of existing as optical isomers

(3) $H_2N(CH_2)_2NH_2$ is a bidentate ligand

(4) the oxidation number of chromium is +3

                 A   B   C   D   E

Give the formula of the octahedral complex containing chromium(III) ions and ammonia molecules.

....

....

15 True statements about this ion, which in its molecular form is known as EDTA, include:

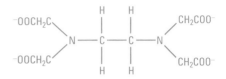

(1) it is likely to act as a tetradentate ligand
(2) it could form a complex of formula [Cu(EDTA)]$^{2-}$ with copper(II) ions
(3) its ability to coordinate to a transition metal ion is enhanced in a more acidic solution
(4) it is likely to act as a hexadentate ligand

▨ A   ▨ B   ▨ C   ▨ D   ▨ E

Write an equation to show the reaction between aqueous copper(II) ions, [Cu(H$_2$O)$_6$]$^{2+}$, and EDTA^{4-} to give the product [Cu(EDTA)]$^{2-}$.

....

....

Questions 16–18 are concerned with the following analysis:
When sodium hydroxide solution was added to a green solution containing a transition metal ion, a green precipitate formed. This precipitate dissolved in excess sodium hydroxide solution, forming another green solution. On warming this solution with hydrogen peroxide, a yellow solution formed.

16 The transition metal in this analysis is likely to be:

▨ A copper
▨ B iron
▨ C vanadium
▨ D manganese
▨ E chromium

What is the colour of the ion [Fe(H$_2$O)$_6$]$^{2+}$?

....

....

17 The ion in the final yellow solution is:

▨ A [Fe(OH)$_4$]$^-$
▨ B CrO$_4$$^{2-}$
▨ C [Cu(OH)$_4$]$^{2-}$
▨ D MnO$_4$$^-$
▨ E VO$_3$$^-$

What is the oxidation number of the transition metal in the yellow solution?

....

....

18 The transition metal featured in the analysis can also form a complex of general formula $[M(NH_3)_4(H_2O)_2]^{3+}$, where M represents the transition metal. Which of statements A–E about this complex is true?

A it can exist as optical isomers

B M has the oxidation state of +2

C it can exist as geometric isomers

D ammonia molecules act as bidentate ligands

E it is likely to be insoluble in water

Starting with the aqueous ion $[M(H_2O)_6]^{3+}$, how can the complex ion in this question be synthesised?

....

....

Enthalpy changes and periodicity

When answering these questions, note that lattice energy is defined as the formation of 1 mol of an ionic solid from its constituent gaseous ions measured at standard conditions.

Questions 1–5 are concerned with the following Born–Haber cycle:

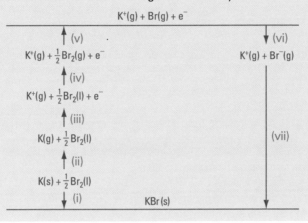

1 The number in the cycle corresponding to the enthalpy of formation for potassium bromide is:

    A (i)   B (ii)   C (iii)   D (iv)   E (v)

Write an equation that relates to the enthalpy of formation of calcium chloride.

....

....

2 The number in the cycle corresponding to the lattice energy for potassium bromide is:

    A (ii)   B (iv)   C (v)   D (vi)   E (vii)

Write an equation that relates to the lattice energy for sodium oxide, Na_2O.

....

....

3 The number in the cycle corresponding to the first ionisation of potassium is:

    A (i)   B (ii)   C (iii)   D (iv)   E (v)

Write an equation to show the second ionisation of potassium.

....

....

4 The number in the cycle corresponding to the electron affinity of bromine is:

    A (ii)   B (iv)   C (v)   D (vi)   E (vii)

Write an equation to show the second electron affinity for bromine.

5 Which of A–E would give the lattice energy for potassium bromide?

- A (i) + (ii) + (iii) + (iv) + (v) + (vi)
- B – (i) – (ii) – (iii) + (iv) + (v) + (vi)
- C (i) – (ii) – (iii) – (iv) – (v) – (vi)
- D (i) + (ii) + (iii) + (iv) + (v) – (vi)
- E (i) + (ii) + (iii) + (iv) – (v) – (vi)

Write an equation for the overall process represented by the enthalpy change (i) – (vii).

Questions 6–9 refer to the following from the Born–Haber cycle for potassium bromide:

Parameter	Energy/kJ mol^{-1}
Enthalpy of formation of KBr(s)	−392
Lattice energy of KBr(s)	−670
Bond energy of the Br–Br bond	+193
First electron affinity for Br(g)	−342
Enthalpy of atomisation of potassium	+90
First ionisation energy of potassium	+418

6 Using the data given above, what is the enthalpy of vaporisation of bromine in kJ mol^{-1}?

- A −81.0
- B +96.5
- C +15.5
- D −20.0
- E +193

Show your working.

7 Consider the equation:

$KBr(s) \longrightarrow K^+(g) + Br(g) + e^-$

The enthalpy change (in kJ mol^{-1}) for this process is:

- A −1012
- B +328
- C +135
- D +1012
- E −328

Show your working.

8 Consider the equation:

$\frac{1}{2}Br_2(g) \longrightarrow Br(g)$

The value of the atomisation energy of bromine is:

A 193
B 193/2
C 193×2
D −193
E 0

Show your working.

9 The hydration energy of the potassium ion is −322 kJ mol^{-1}; that of the bromide ion is −335 kJ mol^{-1}.

What is the enthalpy change (in kJ mol^{-1}) for the process:

$KBr(s) \longrightarrow K^+(aq) + Br^-(aq)$

A +657
B +13.0
C −348
D +670
E −13.0

Show your working.

10 The equation that represents the second electron affinity for oxygen is:

A $O(g) \longrightarrow O^+(g) + e^-$
B $O(g) + e^- \longrightarrow O^-(g)$
C $O^-(g) + e^- \longrightarrow O^{2-}(g)$
D $O^+(g) \longrightarrow O^{2+}(g) + e^-$
E $O_2(g) \longrightarrow 2O(g)$

Why is the second electron affinity for a negatively charged ion always endothermic?

11 Which of the following series is in lattice energy size order, beginning with the least exothermic?

A NaF, NaCl, NaBr
B BeF_2, MgF_2, CaF_2
C Cs_2O, Rb_2O, K_2O
D Al_2O_3, Ga_2O_3, In_2O_3
E MgO, CaO, SrO

What factors determine the magnitude of the lattice energy?

12 The standard enthalpy of formation of methanol, CH_3OH, is represented by:

A $CH_3OH(l) + O_2(g) \longrightarrow CO(g) + 2H_2O(l)$
B $CH_3OH(g) \longrightarrow C(g) + 4H(g) + O(g)$
C $C(s) + 2H_2(g) + \frac{1}{2}O_2(g) \longrightarrow CH_3OH(l)$
D $CH_3OH(l) + \frac{3}{2}O_2(g) \longrightarrow CO_2(g) + 2H_2O(l)$
E $CH_3OH(g) \longrightarrow CO(g) + 2H_2(g)$

Write an equation to show the enthalpy of formation of ethane, $C_2H_6(g)$.

....

....

Instructions for answering questions 13–18:

A 1, 2 and 3 only are correct
B 1 and 3 only are correct
C 2 and 4 only are correct
D 4 only is correct
E some other response

13 True statements about trends from left to right across a period of the periodic table include:
(1) the first electron affinity becomes more negative
(2) electronegativity decreases
(3) the nature of the bonding with chlorine becomes more covalent
(4) atomic radius increases

    A   B   C   D   E

What is the typical variation in the melting point of an element when moving from left to right across a period?

....

....

....

14 Correct statements about the thermal decomposition of magnesium carbonate and barium carbonate include:
(1) at the same temperature, magnesium carbonate decomposes faster than barium carbonate
(2) the magnesium ion is smaller than the barium ion, so the former polarises the carbonate ion more significantly
(3) magnesium carbonate decomposes to form magnesium oxide and carbon dioxide
(4) barium carbonate decomposes to form barium metal

    A   B   C   D   E

Suggest a reason why solid aluminium carbonate does not exist.

....

....

....

15 Formulae for possible oxides of elements in period 3 of the periodic table include:
(1) AlO_2
(2) Na_2O_2
(3) SiO
(4) P_4O_{10} ☐ A ☐ B ☐ C ☐ D ☐ E

Write an equation for the reaction of magnesium oxide with water.

16 True statements about the addition of anhydrous aluminium chloride to excess water include:
(1) a very slow reaction occurs
(2) the complex ion $[Al(H_2O)_6]^{3+}(aq)$ forms
(3) a solution of low pH forms
(4) a hydrolysis occurs ☐ A ☐ B ☐ C ☐ D ☐ E

Write an equation to show the reaction of aluminium with chlorine gas to form aluminium chloride.

17 True statements about the bonding and structure of magnesium oxide and sulphur dioxide include:
(1) magnesium oxide consists of MgO molecules
(2) sulphur dioxide conducts electricity in the molten state
(3) both sulphur dioxide and magnesium oxide are acidic oxides
(4) sulphur dioxide consists of sulphur and oxygen atoms covalently bonded

☐ A ☐ B ☐ C ☐ D ☐ E

Write an equation to show the reaction between sulphur dioxide and water.

18 True statements about electronegativity include:
(1) it decreases down a group of the periodic table
(2) it increases from left to right across period 3
(3) it is the ability of an atom to attract a bonded electron pair
(4) the greater the electronegativity difference between two bonded atoms, the greater the degree of covalent character

☐ A ☐ B ☐ C ☐ D ☐ E

Using electronegativities, explain why the H–F bond is polar.

Rates of reaction

Questions 1–5 relate to graphs A–E, which are all concerned with the reaction, in the presence of a catalyst, between solutions W and X to form a solution Y and a gas Z.

It is known that the rate of reaction depends on the concentrations of W and X according to:

$$\text{rate} \propto [W]^1[X]^0$$

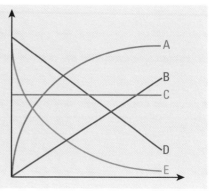

1 Which of graphs A–E best represents a plot of mass of a catalyst (*y*-axis) against time (*x*-axis)?

        A   B   C   D   E

Define a catalyst.

....

....

....

2 Which of graphs A–E best represents a plot of concentration of W (*y*-axis) against time (*x*-axis)?

        A   B   C   D   E

What is special about the half-life for this type of reaction?

....

....

3 Which of graphs A–E best represents a plot of volume of gas Z (*y*-axis) against time (*x*-axis)?

        A   B   C   D   E

In a reaction of this type, where is the reaction rate fastest? Explain your answer.

....

....

....

4 Which of graphs A–E best represents a plot of rate of reaction (*y*-axis) against concentration of W (*x*-axis)?

        A   B   C   D   E

Define rate of reaction mathematically.

....

....

5 Which of graphs A–E best represents a plot of concentration of X with excess W (*y*-axis) against time (*x*-axis)?

        A   B   C   D   E

If rate $\propto [W]^1[X]^0$, what is the overall order of the process?

....

....

Instructions for answering questions 6–11:	A 1, 2 and 3 only are correct
	B 1 and 3 only are correct
	C 2 and 4 only are correct
	D 4 only is correct
	E some other response

6 A rate equation for a reaction is:

    rate = $k[X][Y]^2$

(Concentrations of X and Y are in mol dm^{-3}; rate is measured in mol dm^{-3} s^{-1}.)

True statements include:

(1) k has units of mol^{-2} dm^6 s^{-1}

(2) the value of k changes with time

(3) if the concentrations of both X and Y are doubled, the rate increases by a factor of 8

(4) k will not be affected by an increase in temperature

        A   B   C   D   E

What is the overall order of the process?

....

....

7 With reference to the table, true statements about this reaction include:

(1) the reaction is zero order with respect to the reactant concentration

(2) the reaction has a constant half-life

(3) a graph of reactant concentration against time could be:

(4) a graph of the rate of reaction against reactant concentration could be:

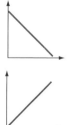

Concentration of reactant/mol dm^{-3}	Time/s
1.000	0
0.500	23
0.250	46
0.125	69
0.063	92

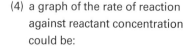

        A   B   C   D   E

Write a rate equation for this process.

....

....

8 True statements about the operation of a catalyst include:

(1) it lowers the activation energy

(2) it participates in the rate-determining step in the mechanism

(3) it provides a new mechanistic route for the reaction

(4) iron in the Haber process is a homogeneous catalyst

    A   B   C   D   E

Explain how using a catalyst in an industrial process reduces operating costs.

....

....

....

9 rate = $k[CH_3COCH_3][H^+][I_2]^0$

True statements about this rate equation include:

(1) it could have been determined from the overall chemical equation

(2) the overall order of the reaction is 2

(3) an iodine molecule, I_2, must be involved in a fast step in the mechanism

(4) the rate constant has units of $mol\,dm^3\,s^{-1}$

    A   B   C   D   E

If all concentrations are doubled, how will the overall rate of reaction be affected?

....

....

10 Reactants X and Y react according the equation:

   $X(aq) + 2Y(aq) \longrightarrow Z(aq)$

Relevant statements about determining the rate equation for the reaction include:

(1) to determine the order with respect to Y, the concentration of X must be in large excess so that the concentration of Y can be monitored with time

(2) the order of reaction with respect to Y is likely to be 2

(3) if the concentrations of X and Y are similar in a reaction, the observed rate of reaction will represent an overall order, not an order with respect to a particular reactant

(4) adding a catalyst to the reaction will result in a different rate equation

    A   B   C   D   E

What is the link, if any, between the balanced chemical equation and the rate equation?

....

....

11 The value of a rate constant, k, can be increased by:

(1) increasing the temperature

(2) increasing the surface area of a solid reactant in a reaction between a solid and a solution

(3) increasing the concentration of a reactant

(4) increasing the total pressure of a gas phase process

   A   B   C   D   E

What are the units of the first-order rate constant if time is measured in seconds?

12 The rate of a reaction $A + B + C \longrightarrow X + Y$ is given by:

$$\text{rate} = k\frac{[A][B]}{[X]}$$

where k is the rate constant and the rate is measured in $\text{mol dm}^{-3}\,\text{s}^{-1}$.

It is true that:

  A the units for the rate constant, k, are $\text{mol}^{-2}\,\text{dm}^6\,\text{s}^{-1}$

  B as [X] increases, the rate of reaction decreases with time

  C X has an autocatalytic effect on the rate of reaction

  D C must be a catalyst for the reaction

  E k will be unchanged with increasing temperature

What is the overall order of this reaction?

Questions 13–15 are concerned with the following experiment: The concentrations of reactants X and Y were varied as shown in the table and the time taken for a reaction to take place was monitored.

[X]	[Y]	Time/s
0.100	0.200	35
0.050	0.200	70
0.030	0.200	105
0.100	0.100	70
0.100	0.067	105

13 With reference to the table, which of A–E gives a measure of the average rate of reaction?

Choice	Average rate
A	[X] × time
B	time
C	1/time taken
D	1/(time taken)^2
E	[Y]

   A   B   C   D   E

If a quantity $P = 1/[X]$, what would be the units of P?

....

....

14 The rate equation for the reaction is:

    A rate $= k[X][Y]^0$

    B rate $= k[X]^0[Y]$

    C rate $= k[X][Y]$

    D rate $= k[X]^2[Y]$

    E rate $= k[X]^0[Y]^2$

What would be the effect on the reaction rate of tripling the concentrations of both X and Y?

....

....

15 When a catalyst, Z, is added to the reaction, the rate equation is:

    rate $= k[X][Y]^0[Z]$

The particle(s) taking part in the rate-determining step are:

    A one Z only

    B one Y only

    C one X and one Z

    D one X, one Z and one Y

    E two Y

Which of the species in the rate equation must be taking part in a fast step in the reaction mechanism?

....

....

Questions 16–18 are concerned with the following graphs:

16 If rate $= k[X]$, which of graphs A–E best satisfies a plot of rate of reaction (y-axis) against [X] (x-axis)?

    A   B   C   D   E

How can the value of k be determined using this graph?

....

....

17 If rate $= k[Y]^0$, which of graphs A–E best satisfies a plot of [Y] (y-axis) against time (x-axis)?

    A   B   C   D   E

Give an equation that describes the graph you have chosen.

....

....

18 If rate = $k[Z]^0$, which of graphs A–E best satisfies a plot of rate of reaction (y-axis) against [Z] (x-axis)?

A   B   C   D   E

What would be the units for k in this rate equation?

....

....

The equilibrium law

1 Consider the reaction:

$C_2H_5OH(l) + CH_3COOH(l) \rightleftharpoons CH_3COOC_2H_5(l) + H_2O(l)$

At a certain temperature, the equilibrium constant, K_c, for this reaction is 4.00. At equilibrium, there are 0.010 mol of C_2H_5OH, 0.020 mol of CH_3COOH and 0.030 mol of $CH_3COOC_2H_5$. How many moles of H_2O are present at equilibrium?

     A 0.027
     B 2.40×10^{-5}
     C 4.06
     D 600
     E 6.67×10^7

Show your working.

....

....

....

....

2 Consider the reaction:

$2NO_2(g) \rightleftharpoons N_2O_4(g)$

The equilibrium constant expression for K_c for this reaction is:

     A $\dfrac{[N_2O_4]}{[NO_2]^2}$

     B $[N_2O_4] + [NO_2]^2$

     C $\dfrac{[NO_2]^2}{[N_2O_4]}$

     D $\dfrac{p(N_2O_4)}{p(NO_2)}$

     E $\dfrac{p(N_2O_4)}{p(NO_2)^2}$

What are the units for K_c for this reaction?

....

....

3 Consider the reaction:

$CO(g) + Cl_2(g) \rightleftharpoons COCl_2(g)$

The partial pressures (in atm) of carbon monoxide, chlorine gas and phosgene are 2.0, 4.9 and 1.2 respectively. The value for the equilibrium constant K_p for this reaction is:

A 0.49

B 0.12

C 2.0

D 8.1

E 8.3

Show your working.

4 The dissociation of water is given by:

$2H_2O(l) \rightleftharpoons H_3O^+(aq) + OH^-(aq)$

If the value for the equilibrium constant, K_w, is 10^{-14} mol^2 dm^{-6} at 298 K, what is the concentration of $[H_3O^+]$ at equilibrium?

A 10^{-14}

B 10^{-12}

C 10^{-10}

D 10^{-7}

E 10^{-4}

Show your working.

5 Consider the reaction:

$CO(g) + H_2O(g) \rightleftharpoons CO_2(g) + H_2(g)$

Given that the amounts (in mol) at equilibrium of carbon monoxide, steam, carbon dioxide and hydrogen are 2.4×10^{-5}, 2.5×10^{-5}, 1.2×10^{-4} and 3.6×10^{-5} respectively, what is the value for the equilibrium constant, K_c, for this reaction?

A 0.14

B 0.72

C 0.98

D 7.2

E 14

Show your working.

6 What are the units for K_c in the following expression?

$$K_c = \frac{[NO]^2[O_2]}{[NO_2]^2}$$

A mol dm^{-3}

B mol^2 dm^{-6}

C mol^{-1} dm^3

D mol^{-2} dm^6

E mol^3 dm^{-9}

What factor(s) affect the magnitude of K_c?

7 Consider the reaction:

$N_2O_4(g) \rightleftharpoons 2NO_2(g)$

1.00 mol of N_2O_4 is allowed to dissociate at 5.00 atm pressure and it is found that 0.20 mol of N_2O_4 remains at equilibrium. What is the value for the equilibrium constant, K_p?

A 0.125
B 8.00
C 0.0156
D 35.2
E 64.0

Show your working.

8 Consider the reaction:

$3O_2(g) \rightleftharpoons 2O_3(g)$ $K_c = 2.40 \times 10^{-3} \, mol^{-1} \, dm^3$

If the concentration of oxygen gas is $1.60 \times 10^{-3} \, mol \, dm^{-3}$, the corresponding concentration (in $mol \, dm^{-3}$) of ozone, O_3, is:

A 9.83
B 1.96×10^{-3}
C 3.14×10^{-6}
D 9.83×10^{-12}
E 3.19×10^5

Show your working.

9 Consider the general reaction:

$W(g) + 3X(g) \rightleftharpoons Y(g) + 2Z(g)$

When 1 mol each of W and X are mixed and allowed to come to equilibrium, x mol of Y forms. How many moles of X are left at equilibrium?

A $1 - x$
B $3x$
C x
D $1 - 3x$
E $3 - 3x$

If x is 0.2 mol, how many moles of W, X, Y and Z are present at equilibrium?

10 0.200 mol of gas X and 0.600 mol of gas Y are mixed together at a total pressure of 20.0 atm. What is the partial pressure (in atm) of X in the mixture?

A 0.250
B 0.800
C 4.00
D 5.00
E 20.0

Show your working.

....

....

Instructions for answering questions 11–18:

A 1, 2 and 3 only are correct
B 1 and 3 only are correct
C 2 and 4 only are correct
D 4 only is correct
E some other response

11 Essential features of a system at equilibrium include:
(1) matter is not allowed to escape or enter the system
(2) the forward rate of reaction is faster than the reverse rate
(3) the concentrations of reactants and products do not vary with time
(4) the concentrations of reactants and products are equal

| A | B | C | D | E |

How does an increase in pressure affect the rate at which an equilibrium is attained *and* the value of the equilibrium constant?

....

....

12 Consider the reaction:

$$CH_3COOH(aq) + H_2O(l) \rightleftharpoons CH_3COO^-(aq) + H_3O^+(aq)$$

Which of the following will result in the equilibrium position for the reaction moving to the left?
(1) adding more water
(2) adding solid potassium ethanoate, $CH_3COO^-K^+$
(3) adding solid sodium carbonate, Na_2CO_3
(4) adding concentrated hydrochloric acid

| A | B | C | D | E |

If the dissociation of ethanoic acid is exothermic, what effect, if any, will increasing the temperature have on the rate at which equilibrium is attained *and* on the pH of the equilibrium mixture?

....

....

....

13 Consider the reaction:

$$N_2(g) + 3H_2(g) \rightleftharpoons 2NH_3(g)$$

Which of the following will increase the yield of ammonia?
(1) increasing the total pressure
(2) removing the ammonia as soon as it is formed
(3) adding more nitrogen gas at constant volume
(4) adding a catalyst

A   B   C   D   E

Write an expression for K_c for the reverse process: $2NH_3(g) \rightleftharpoons N_2(g) + 3H_2(g)$
....
....

14 The rate at which a gas phase equilibrium is attained is increased by:
(1) increasing the temperature
(2) doubling the volume but keeping the mass of gas the same
(3) increasing the total pressure
(4) adding a catalyst   A   B   C   D   E

What conditions are used in the Haber process to increase the rate at which ammonia is formed?
....
....

15 Which of the following affect the value of an equilibrium constant?
(1) total pressure in a gas phase reaction
(2) concentration of a reactant
(3) temperature
(4) a catalyst   A   B   C   D   E

Write an expression for the equilibrium constant, K_c, for the reaction $2NO(g) \rightleftharpoons N_2O_2(g)$
....
....

Questions 16–18 are concerned with the reaction:

$$2SO_2(g) + O_2(g) \rightleftharpoons 2SO_3(g)$$

Equilibrium data are given in the table.

Temperature/K	K_p/atm^{-1}
298	4.0×10^{24}
500	2.5×10^{10}
700	3.0×10^{4}

16 Correct statements about the equilibrium constant, K_p, for this reaction include:
(1) its value decreases with increasing temperature
(2) the values for K_p show that formation of SO_2 is favoured at higher temperatures
(3) K_p for the reverse reaction ($2SO_3(g) \rightleftharpoons 2SO_2(g) + O_2(g)$) is equal to $1/K_p$ for the forward process
(4) increasing the total pressure causes more SO_3 to form, so K_p increases

A   B   C   D   E

Write an expression for the equilibrium constant, K_p, for this reaction.

17 From the data, it can be suggested that:
(1) the equilibrium position shifts to the right on increasing the temperature
(2) the enthalpy change for the forward reaction is endothermic
(3) the rate of only the forward process increases with increasing temperature
(4) over the temperature range 298–700 K, products dominate the equilibrium mixture

        A   B   C   D   E

When the temperature is increased, what factor determines the direction in which the equilibrium position moves?

18 True statements about the rates of the forward and reverse processes in this reaction include:
(1) they are equal when the process is at equilibrium
(2) a catalyst will increase both the forward and reverse rates equally
(3) as the temperature increases, the rates of the forward and reverse reactions both increase
(4) the rate at which equilibrium is attained will decrease when the total pressure is increased

        A   B   C   D   E

How does a catalyst increase the rate at which an equilibrium is attained?

Acid–base equilibria

In all calculations, assume that $K_w = 1.00 \times 10^{-14}\ mol^2\ dm^{-6}$.

Instructions for answering questions 1–5:	A 1, 2 and 3 only are correct
	B 1 and 3 only are correct
	C 2 and 4 only are correct
	D 4 only is correct
	E some other response

1 Which of the following are *not* normally considered to be Brønsted–Lowry acids?

(1) HNO_3

(2) CH_3NH_2

(3) CH_3COOH

(4) CH_4 A   B   C   D   E

Write an equation to show the complete dissociation of sulphuric acid in water.

....

....

2 True statements about a $1.00\,mol\,dm^{-3}$ solution of ethanoic acid, CH_3COOH, include:

(1) the concentration of ethanoate ions, CH_3COO^-, is $1.00\,mol\,dm^{-3}$

(2) at equilibrium, most of the acid is undissociated

(3) ethanoic acid is a strong acid

(4) the ethanoate ion is the conjugate base of ethanoic acid

     A   B   C   D   E

When more water is added, what happens to the percentage of ethanoic acid that is dissociated?

....

....

3 Which of the following form a buffer system when added to a solution of ammonia?

(1) H_2O

(2) NH_4Cl

(3) $NaNO_3$

(4) NH_4NO_3 A   B   C   D   E

Define a buffer solution.

....

....

4 In an experiment, $50.0\,cm^3$ of $2.00\,mol\,dm^{-3}$ sulphuric acid are added to $50.0\,cm^3$ of $2.00\,mol\,dm^{-3}$ sodium hydroxide solution. Correct statements about this reaction include:

(1) the resulting solution will have a pH less than 7

(2) the pH of the resulting solution will be equal, or close, to 7

(3) in the resulting solution, sodium hydroxide will be in excess

(4) the ionic equation for the reaction is $H_3O^+(aq) + OH^-(aq) \longrightarrow 2H_2O(l)$

     A   B   C   D   E

Write an equation for the reaction between sulphuric acid and copper(II) oxide.

....

....

5 True statements about an acid–base indicator that has a pK_{ind} value of 4.30, a red acidic form and a yellow basic form, include:

   (1) the relative proportions of acid and basic forms of the indicator are dependent on the pH of the solution
   (2) at a pH of 4.30, the indicator will be orange
   (3) at a high pH, the indicator will be yellow
   (4) if dilute hydrochloric acid is added to the indicator solution, the indicator turns red

A   B   C   D   E

How does pH affect the colour of an indicator?

....

....

....

....

Questions 6–9 are concerned with the following experiment.

   10.00 cm³ of sulphuric acid of unknown concentration was titrated with sodium hydroxide solution of unknown concentration. The following titration curve was obtained:

pH (y-axis, 0 to 14) versus Volume of NaOH(aq) (x-axis, 0 to 25).

6 The approximate concentration (in mol dm⁻³) of the sulphuric acid solution at the start of the experiment was:

    A 3.00
    B 0.032
    C 0.016
    D 0.064
    E 1.50

Show your working.

....

....

....

....

7 From the titration curve, what approximate volume of sodium hydroxide solution (cm³) is required to completely neutralise the sulphuric acid?

A 7.50
B 15.0
C 20.0
D 22.5
E 25.0

What is the pH at equivalence in this particular titration?

....

....

8 Using the volume of sodium hydroxide solution for complete neutralisation, what is the approximate concentration (in mol dm⁻³) of the sodium hydroxide solution used?

A 0.005
B 0.010
C 0.015
D 0.020

Show your working.

....

....

....

....

....

9 With reference to the table, which indicator would *not* be suitable for this titration?

Choice	Indicator	pH range
A	Thymol blue	1.2–2.8
B	Phenol red	6.8–8.4
C	Methyl red	4.2–6.3
D	Phenolphthalein	8.3–10.0
E	Thymolphthalein	9.3–10.5

A   B   C   D   E

pK_{ind} for an indicator X is 3.50. What are the proportions of the acid and base forms of the indicator at pH 3.50?

....

....

10 A solution of a weak acid of concentration 1.20 mol dm⁻³ is found to have a pH of 2.20. An approximate value of K_a (mol dm⁻³) for the acid is:

A 0.65
B 130
C 3.3×10^{-5}
D 2.1×10^4
E 5.3×10^{-3}

Show your working.

11 The pH of the solution formed when 24.90 cm^3 of
1.00 mol dm^{-3} hydrochloric acid is added to 25.00 cm^3
of 1.00 mol dm^{-3} sodium hydroxide is:

    A 2.7
    B 4.5
    C 7.0
    D 9.2
    E 11.3

Show your working.

12 What will be the pOH of a solution that has a hydrogen
ion concentration of 2.32×10^{-5} mol dm^{-3}?

    A 9.4
    B 0.36
    C 4.6
    D 0.72
    E 2.3

Show your working.

13 An acid, HA, has an acid dissociation constant, pK_a, of
4.30. In a solution of HA of concentration 0.500 mol dm^{-3},
what approximate percentage of HA molecules will have
dissociated?

    A 5×10^{-5}
    B 5×10^{-3}
    C 0.5
    D 1
    E 10

Show your working.

....

....

....

....

14 The formula of the conjugate base of sulphuric acid is:

    A SO_3
    B HSO_4^{2-}
    C HSO_4^-
    D SO_2
    E SO_3^{2-}

Give the formula of the conjugate acid of ammonia, NH_3.

....

....

15 Which of the following expressions is equal to the ionic product of water, K_w?

    A $[H_3O^+]\times[OH^-]^2$
    B $[H_3O^+] + [OH^-]$
    C $[H_3O^+]\times[OH^-]$
    D $\dfrac{[H_3O^+] + [OH^-]}{[H_3O^+]\times[OH^-]}$
    E $[H_3O^+] - [OH^-]$

How is the value K_w expected to vary with increasing temperature?

....

....

16 A solution has a pH of 13.45. The concentration (in $mol\,dm^{-3}$) of hydroxide ions in this solution is:

    A 0.28
    B 1.12
    C 3.5×10^{-14}
    D 1.35
    E 0.55

Show your working.

....

....

17 In a buffer solution, the concentrations of ethanoic acid and sodium ethanoate are $0.0200\,mol\,dm^{-3}$ and $0.0100\,mol\,dm^{-3}$ respectively. What is the approximate pH of the buffer solution? (pK_a for ethanoic acid = 4.76)

    A 5.06
    B 4.45
    C 0.087
    D 8.93
    E −1.06

Show your working.

....

....

....

....

....

18 What is the pH of a solution of methanoic acid, HCOOH, of concentration 0.60 mol dm^{-3}? (pK_a for methanoic acid = 3.75)

- A 0.99
- B 1.99
- C 2.52
- D 3.97
- E 3.75

Show your working.

....

....

....

....

General questions

In all calculations, assume that $K_w = 1.00 \times 10^{-14}$ (with appropriate units).

1 The exothermic lattice energy for calcium chloride is represented by:

- A $Ca^+(g) + Cl^-(g) \longrightarrow CaCl(s)$
- B $Ca^{2+}(g) + 2Cl^-(g) \longrightarrow CaCl_2(aq)$
- C $Ca^{2+}(g) + 2Cl^-(g) \longrightarrow CaCl_2(s)$
- D $Ca(s) + Cl_2(g) \longrightarrow CaCl_2(s)$
- E $Ca(g) + 2Cl(g) \longrightarrow CaCl_2(g)$

Write an equation that relates to the exothermic lattice energy for sodium fluoride, NaF.

....

....

2 A weak acid has an acid dissociation constant, pK_a, of 4.15. The value of K_a (in mol dm^{-3}) is:

- A −4.15
- B 9.9
- C −0.62
- D 7.1×10^{-5}
- E 1.4×10^4

Show your working.

3 Consider the reaction:

$$C_2H_4(g) + H_2O(g) \rightleftharpoons C_2H_5OH(g)$$

The expression for the equilibrium constant, K_c, for this reaction is:

A $\dfrac{[C_2H_4] + [H_2O]}{[C_2H_5OH]}$

B $p(C_2H_5OH) - p(C_2H_4) - p(H_2O)$

C $\dfrac{[C_2H_5OH]}{[C_2H_4] \times [H_2O]}$

D $\dfrac{p(C_2H_5OH)}{p(C_2H_4) \times p(H_2O)}$

E $\dfrac{[C_2H_5OH]}{[C_2H_4]}$

What are the units of K_c in this reaction?

4 The initial rate for the reaction between X and Y doubles when the concentration of reactant X doubles; it increases by a factor of 27 when the concentration of reactant Y triples. The rate equation for the process is:

A rate = $k[A][B]^0$

B rate = $k[A][B]$

C rate = $k[A]^2[B]$

D rate = $k[A][B]^2$

E rate = $k[A][B]^3$

What are the units for the rate constant?

5 When added to an aqueous solution of benzoic acid, C_6H_5COOH, which of substances A–E would produce an acid–base buffer?

A $CH_3COOH(l)$

B $HCl(aq)$

C $C_6H_5COONa(s)$

D $NH_4Cl(s)$

E $C_2H_5OH(l)$

Write an equation to show how benzoic acid dissociates in water.

6 Consider the reaction:

$$N_2(g) + 3H_2(g) \rightleftharpoons 2NH_3(g)$$

In the Haber process, the equilibrium partial pressures (in atm) are: $p(N_2) = 2.20$, $p(H_2) = 4.60$ and $p(NH_3) = 10.72$. The value of K_p for this reaction is:

A 1.06

B 5.07×10^3

C 11.3

D 0.54

E 1.89

Show your working.

7 What is the pH of a buffer solution containing
1.20 mol dm^{-3} ethanoic acid and 0.300 mol dm^{-3} sodium
ethanoate? (pK_a for ethanoic acid = 4.76)

- A 2.00
- B 4.76
- C 5.06
- D 3.47
- E 4.16

Show your working.

8 Which of chlorides A–E is extensively hydrolysed when
added to water?

- A NaCl
- B $CaCl_2$
- C $CuCl_2$
- D KCl
- E $AlCl_3$

Write an equation for this hydrolysis.

9 What is the pH of the solution formed when 20.10 cm^3 of
0.5 mol dm^{-3} sodium hydroxide solution is added to
20.00 cm^3 of 0.5 mol dm^{-3} hydrochloric acid?

- A 0.30
- B 4.30
- C 2.90
- D 7.00
- E 11.1

Show your working.

10 The units for the ionic product for water, K_w, are:

    A mol dm^{-3}
    B mol^2 dm^{-6}
    C mol dm^3
    D mol^{-1} dm^3
    E mol^{-1} dm^{-3}

Show your working.

....

....

Instructions for answering questions 11–15:	A 1, 2 and 3 only are correct
	B 1 and 3 only are correct
	C 2 and 4 only are correct
	D 4 only is correct
	E some other response

11 Equilibria that have an equilibrium position unaffected by an increase in pressure include:

(1) $2HI(g) \rightleftharpoons H_2(g) + I_2(g)$
(2) $NH_3(g) \rightleftharpoons \frac{1}{2}N_2(g) + \frac{3}{2}H_2(g)$
(3) $2NO(g) \rightleftharpoons N_2(g) + O_2(g)$
(4) $N_2O_4(g) \rightleftharpoons 2NO_2(g)$

    A   B   C   D   E

In all cases, what effect does increasing the pressure have on the rate at which equilibrium is attained?

....

....

12 A pH titration curve similar to that shown would be produced by:

(1) $NH_3(aq)$ and $CH_3COOH(aq)$
(2) $CH_3COOH(aq)$ and $NaOH(aq)$
(3) $HCl(aq)$ and $NaOH(aq)$
(4) $C_6H_5COOH(aq)$ and $KOH(aq)$

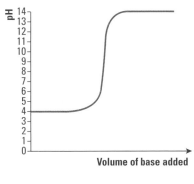

    A   B   C   D   E

In this titration, what is the approximate pH at equivalence?

....

....

13 Which of the indicators in the table would be suitable for the titration featured in Question 12?

Choice	Indicator	pH range
(1)	Phenol red	6.8–8.4
(2)	Methyl red	4.2–6.3
(3)	Phenolphthalein	8.3–10.0
(4)	Thymol blue	1.2–2.8

▨ A   ▨ B   ▨ C   ▨ D   ▨ E

Using HIn to represent the formula of a general indicator, write an equation to show how HIn dissociates in water.

....

....

14 In which of these rate equations does the rate constant have units of $mol^{-2}\ dm^6\ s^{-1}$?
(1) Rate = $k[A]^2[B]$
(2) Rate = $k[A]^2$
(3) Rate = $k[B]^3$
(4) Rate = $k[A][B]^0$ ▨ A   ▨ B   ▨ C   ▨ D   ▨ E

What is the overall order of the reaction that has a rate equation: rate = $k[A]^2[B]$?

....

....

15 Which of the following would produce a similar graph to the one shown?

Choice	Quantity on y-axis	Quantity on x-axis
(1)	Rate	Temperature
(2)	Rate	Concentration for a zero-order process
(3)	Rate	Concentration for a second-order process
(4)	Rate	Concentration for a first-order process

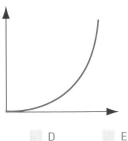

▨ A   ▨ B   ▨ C   ▨ D   ▨ E

What are the units of a second-order rate constant?

....

....

16 The second ionisation of magnesium is represented by:

▨ A $Mg(g) + 2e^- \longrightarrow Mg^{2-}(g)$
▨ B $Mg(s) \longrightarrow Mg^{2+}(aq) + 2e^-$
▨ C $Mg^+(g) \longrightarrow Mg^{2+}(g) + e^-$
▨ D $Mg(s) \longrightarrow Mg^+(aq) + e^-$
▨ E $Mg^+(aq) \longrightarrow Mg^{2+}(aq) + 2e^-$

Describe the changes in ionisation energy of magnesium, as all 12 electrons are removed.

17 When a spatula measure of sodium chloride,
NaCl, is added to a small test-tube containing
water, the approximate pH of the resulting
solution is:

A 1
B 3
C 5
D 7
E 11

Write an equation to show the dissolving of sodium chloride in water.

18 Which of A–E possesses the most exothermic
lattice energy?

A LiCl
B NaCl
C KCl
D RbCl
E CsCl

Which of NaCl or MgO possesses more exothermic lattice energy? Explain your answer.

Philip Allan Updates, Market Place, Deddington, Oxfordshire, OX15 0SE

Orders

Bookpoint Ltd, 130 Milton Park, Abingdon, Oxfordshire, OX14 4SB
tel: 01235 827720   fax: 01235 400454   e-mail: uk.orders@bookpoint.co.uk

Lines are open 9.00 a.m.–5.00 p.m., Monday to Saturday, with a 24-hour
message answering service. You can also order through the Philip Allan
Updates website: www.philipallan.co.uk

© Philip Allan Updates 2004

ISBN-13: 978-1-84489-111-5   ISBN-10: 1-84489-111-9

Printed in Spain

Philip Allan Updates' policy is to use papers that are natural, renewable
and recyclable products and made from wood grown in sustainable forests.
The logging and manufacturing processes are expected to conform to the
environmental regulations of the country of origin.